SCIENCE THEORY
AND MAN

SCIENCE THEORY
AND MAN

FORMERLY PUBLISHED UNDER
THE TITLE
'SCIENCE AND THE HUMAN TEMPERAMENT'

ERWIN SCHROEDINGER
NOBEL LAUREATE

Ruskin House
GEORGE ALLEN AND UNWIN LTD
MUSEUM STREET LONDON

CONTENTS

*

PREFACE

I AM glad to write a few words by way of preface to the volume written by Professor Erwin Schrö-dinger, translated by Mr. James Murphy. I do so with the greater pleasure that the author is now domiciled in this country and is sharing in our scientific life.

As is well known, Professor Schrödinger took an important part in the development of the new theories which have proved so successful in the interpretation of atomic phenomena. It is thus of special interest to have his views on the effect of these theories on the fundamental conceptions underlying our interpretation of the material world. This problem is considered from different angles in a number of addresses in this volume, including a discussion on the laws of chance and the principle of indeterminism, and the meaning of a law of Nature. The last chapter, containing the address given by him in Stockholm on the occasion of the award of a Nobel Prize last year, is of much interest, for it brings out in a striking way the relations between the new and older ideas, and the possible reconciliation between the different aspects of Nature involved in the particle and wave conceptions of matter. On these fundamental questions involving the meaning and scope of the law of causality there is room for much difference of opinion but many in this country, whether they agree with the author or not, will read these charming and simply-written essays with much pleasure and interest.

RUTHERFORD,
Cambridge, Feb. 19, 1935.

BIOGRAPHICAL
INTRODUCTION
BY JAMES MURPHY

I MADE the notes for this Introduction on a summer afternoon while roaming in the churchyard
of Cloyne Cathedral, a place which has been familiar
to me since childhood. As everybody knows, it was
here that the great Bishop Berkeley had his See.
Nearby, in what is now the deanery, he lived for
twenty years. His ecclesiastical duties were light, because there were only very few members of the
established Protestant Church in this part of Ireland.
The Episcopal See of Cloyne was therefore a fitting
source of livelihood for a philosopher and the surroundings were ideal.

Only a small distance from the cathedral the old
Norman castle still stands, festooned now with a pro-
fusion of ivy, in whose branches thousands of birds
have made their nests. This is probably the original
of the castle which Berkeley mentions in the *Dialogues.* The passage is worth quoting here, because
it has a very close bearing on what I shall have to say
later on.

EUPHRANOR: Tell me, Alciphron, can you discern
the doors, window and battlements of that same
castle?

ALCIPHRON: I cannot. At this distance it seems
only a small round tower.

EUPHRANOR: But I, who have been at it, know
that it is no small round tower, but a large
square building with battlements and turrets,
which it seems you do not see.

ALCIPHRON: What will you infer from thence?

EUPHRANOR: I would infer that the very object
which you strictly and properly perceive by
sight is not that thing which is several miles distant.

He clinches the argument further on by saying: "Is it
not plain therefore, that neither the castle, the planet,

nor the cloud, which you see here, are those real ones which you suppose to exist at a distance?"

In these few passages we have a clear indication of Berkeley's attitude towards the epistemological question that is agitating the minds of scientists in our own day. And I have called attention to Berkeley here because the trend of theoretical physics to-day, in its search for a definite epistemological standpoint, is somewhat in the nature of a pilgrimage to the Cathedral of Cloyne. This is why Berkeley is referred to and quoted so largely by British physicists—Jeans, Eddington and Whitehead, for instance—who are anxious to find philosophical justification for their own attitude towards the latest theories in atomic physics. I am confident that he would be referred to also by Professor Schroedinger in the present book, if Schroedinger had been as familiar with the writings of the Irish philosopher as he is with those of the Irish scientist, Sir William Hamilton, to whom he is so very largely indebted for the basic inspiration of his own mathematical work. The key to much of what Schroedinger writes in the following chapters, about the difficulties of the epistemological problem in quantum mechanics as a whole and especially in wave mechanics, will be found in Berkeley. As this book is written for the lay reader, and as the lay approach to modern theoretical physics is mostly from the philosophical side, I have thought it well to direct attention to this source of philosophical clarity at the very outset.

Let us now turn to Schroedinger and his work. What place does he hold in the history of physical science and what is the relative importance of that place? In other words, what has he achieved and to what further developments are his achievements likely to lead, whether in his own hands or in those of his colleagues?

Erwin Schroedinger is a native of Austria. He was born at Vienna forty-seven years ago. He studied mathematical physics at the University of Vienna, attending the branch of that institution known as The Physical Institute. Of this Institute Ludwig Boltzmann had been the inspiring genius and the founder of its special tradition. He had just died when Schroedinger became a student there. Boltzmann, of course, was responsible for some of the most fundamental ideas on which modern theoretical physics is based. He it was who first gave a statistical formulation to the heat theorem which is now called The Second Law of Thermodynamics. In doing so he introduced for the first time into exact natural science a statistical law, to replace the strict one of cause and effect.

In 1921 Schroedinger was appointed Professor of Mathematical Physics in the University of Zurich. While there he propounded his theory of wave mechanics and published what is known as the Schroedinger wave equation.

"This equation," says Max Planck, "has provided the basis of modern Quantum-mechanics, in which it seems to play the same part as do the equations established by Newton, Lagrange and Hamilton, in classical mechanics." [1] In 1926 Max Planck resigned the Chair of Theoretical Physics in the University of Berlin but remained *Bestaendiger Sekretar* of the Prussian Academy of Science. Schroedinger was called from Zurich to succeed Planck at the Berlin University.

He told me his own story during the course of an address delivered before the Prussian Academy of Science on the occasion of his inauguration to membership of that body (July 4th, 1929). He said:—

"In expressing my sincere appreciation of the distinction which you have conferred on me to-day by electing me a member of the Academy of Science I

---

[1] *The Universe in the Light of Modern Physics*, page 29.

must say that it is a particular pleasure for me to see at our head, still in the full vigor of his powers, the master whom we all revere and whose successor in the professorial chair I have the honor to be. I may presume that his opinion decidedly influenced you in electing me.

"Allow me, first of all, to discharge as briefly as possible the unpleasant task which an academic inaugural address involves, namely, that of speaking of myself.

"The old Vienna Institute, which had just mourned the tragic loss of Ludwig Boltzmann, the building where Fritz Hasenoehrl and Franz Exner carried on their work and where I saw many others of Boltzmann's students coming and going, gave me a direct insight into the ideas which had been formulated by that great mind. His line of thought may be called my first love in science. No other has ever thus enraptured me or will ever do so again. Only very slowly did I approach the modern atomic theory. Its inherent contradictions sounded harsh and crude, when compared with the pure and inexorably clear development of Boltzmann's reasoning. I even, as it were, fled from it for a while and, inspired by Franz Exner and K. W. F. Kohlrausch, I took refuge in the sphere of

color theory. As to atomic theory, I tested and rejected many an attempt (partly of my own, partly of
others) to restore at least clarity of thought even at
the expense of a most revolutionary change. The first
to bring a certain relief was de Broglie's idea of electron waves, which I developed into the theory of wave
mechanics. But we are still pretty far from really
grasping the new way of comprehending nature which
has been initiated on the one hand by wave mechanics
and, on the other, by Heisenberg's Quantum mechanics."

He went on to say that the aim of physics must be
to discover the fewest possible simple and fundamental laws to which each single phenomenon in the
mass of complex empirical phenomena may be referred. Classical mechanics followed this aim and
achieved magnificent results. This led to the idea of
extending the mechanical method to all branches of
physics and trying to explain every natural process by
making a model of it. But nowadays, with the advance
of Quantum physics, this idea has to be abandoned.
The burning question here is the utility of the general
principle of causality.

"It is true," he said, "that in practice we had had
to forgo the use of causality even within that aspect

of nature that was based on classical mechanics. To me personally this fact is connected in my mind with a very deep impression that I received as a young man when I heard the inaugural address delivered by Fritz Hasenoehrl, of whom an untimely fate robbed us in the war, and to whom I owe my whole scientific outlook. It would not contradict the laws of nature, Hasenoehrl declared, if this piece of wood should lift itself into the air without any ostensible cause. According to the mechanical aspect of nature such a miracle, being a reversion of the opposite process, would not be impossible but only extremely unlikely. Yet the concept of probability being involved in the laws of nature, which Hasenoehrl had in his mind when he used these words, does not really contradict the causal postulate. Uncertainty in this case arises only from the practical impossibility of determining the initial state of a body composed of billions of atoms. To-day, however, the doubt as to whether the processes of nature are absolutely determined is of quite a different character. The difficulty of ascertaining the initial state is supposed to be not one of practice but of principle. It is supposed to affect not merely a complicated system, but even a single atom or molecule. Since what is by no possible means observable does not exist for the physicist as a physicist, the meaning clearly is, that not even the elementary system is so exactly defined as to let it react to a definite influence by a definite behavior.

"Franz Exner, to whom I am personally indebted for unusually great encouragement, was the first to mention the possibility and the advisability of an acausal concept of nature. This he did in the lectures which he published in 1919. Since 1926 the same question has arisen under a new point of view in the quantum theory. Indeed it appears to be of fundamental importance. But I do not believe that in this form it will ever be answered. In my opinion this question does not involve a decision as to what the real character of a natural happening is, but rather as to whether the one or the other predisposition of mind be the more useful and convenient one with which to approach nature. Henri Poincaré explained that we are free to apply Euclidian or any kind of non-Euclidian geometry we like to real space, without having to fear the contradiction of facts. But the physical laws which we are going to discuss are a function of the geometry which we have applied, and it may be that the one geometry entails complicated laws, the other much simpler ones. In that case the former geometry is inconvenient, the latter is convenient, but the words 'right' and 'wrong' are unsuitable. The same statement probably applies to the postulate of rigid causality. We can hardly imagine any experimental facts which would finally decide whether Nature is absolutely determined or is partially indetermined. The most that can be decided is whether the one or the other concept leads to the simpler and clearer survey of all the observed facts. Even this question will probably take a long time to decide; for the question of world geometry also has been rendered the more doubtful by Poincaré's having made us aware of the fact that we have the liberty of choice."

The trend of thought which underlies the last paragraph is that which has inspired almost every chapter of the present book. Perhaps this is the best place to explain how the book as it now stands came to be written.

In the summer of 1932, a few days before my departure from Berlin after a residence of some years there, Schroedinger and myself foregathered for tea in one of the cafés in Unter den Linden. We discussed the feasibility of making a book out of some of the papers which he had written from time to time and some of the lectures which he had delivered on special occasions. On looking over the heterogeneous material I then felt that there would be a certain amount of difficulty in grouping it so as to form an organic whole. Therefore we allowed the project to drop for the time being. It was not resumed until Schroedinger had left Germany, in 1933, and taken a temporary position at the University of Oxford. Meanwhile he had been awarded the Nobel Prize in Physics for 1933, and moreover he was now able to place some additional material at my disposal.

Some of the papers that have been incorporated in this book are chiefly of historical interest, as they indicate Schroedinger's relation to the progress which has recently been made in the theoretical development of physical science. For that reason they have been translated quite literally and I have assigned to them the dates and occasions on which they were written or delivered. Perhaps I ought to say here that Professor Schroedinger has been in England while the present book was being written and has worked over my version of the original; so that the English style is in a sense the result of a joint enterprise.

The chapter entitled *What is a Law of Nature?* calls for some special mention. The original was the inaugural address delivered by Professor Schroedinger on the occasion of his appointment to the Chair of Physics in the University of Zurich. We have to understand the circumstances of the time in order to appreciate the importance of his pronouncement. It was an exposition of Franz Exner's view in favor of a systematic departure from the mechanical concept of cause and effect. When the new idea was first broached by Exner it made little or no impression on the great body of scientists in Germany, France and the Scandinavian and Netherland countries. Schroedinger's presentation of it may be said to mark, in a certain sense, the opening of a new epoch in physical science.

In 1927 Heisenberg promulgated his Uncertainty Principle. Of this event Sir Arthur Eddington writes: "It was Heisenberg again who set in motion the new development in the summer of 1927. The outcome of it is a fundamental general principle which seems to rank in importance with the principle of relativity."[1] Heisenberg's development of Quantum Mechanics during the years immediately preceding, and the culmination of that development in the 1927 pronouncement, gradually led to the radical modification of the

---

[1] The Nature of the Physical World, page 220.

Rutherford-Bohr model of the atom. This model, the reader will remember, pictured the atom as a sort of miniature solar system, with a fixed nucleus around which the electrons spin in various kinds of orbits.

In the chapter on the value of conceptual models Schroedinger deals with the views put forward by Professor Dirac. That was partly the theme of his address before the Frankfort Physical Society in 1929. In order to understand the significance of this chapter in the present book we must place it in its historical perspective. Schroedinger deals with what seem to be the logical consequences of Heisenberg's statement, though he does not actually accept these consequences. He leaves the matter undecided. Yet it is quite clear that he has a distinct leaning towards that line of thought and it is clear too that his own work has contributed to bring that line of thought into the foreground of modern science. We may put the general idea thus:

If it be true that, in microscopic physics, we are prevented by the nature of things from being able to ascertain the location and velocity of a particle at one and the same instant we cannot, of course, predict with certainty a subsequent state of that particle. In other words, as we cannot ascertain the place and speed of an electron at the same instant it is impossible accurately to compute the future path of the electron. Any interference on our part would change the position of the electron itself. Therefore we must abandon the application of the causal connection here. Whether or not the causal connection be true in reality is a question that has no meaning for the physicist, for the simple reason that in physics he cannot apply it. Now if we are to abandon the causal structure we must obviously abandon the mechanical structure. We must turn to the statistical concept. And this means that we must turn absolutely and entirely to the purely mathematical concept. In other words, Schroedinger pleads for the abandonment of what may be called mechanicomorphism in the pursuit of natural science, just as a former generation of scientists had successfully pleaded for the abandonment of anthropomorphism in the study of nature. The casting aside of all models and the wholesale employment of mathematical formulas in their stead, because the latter are found more suitable for the representation of what is called ultimate physical reality, comes very close to the Berkeleian standpoint and, in the theory of wave mechanics, reduces the last building stones of the universe to something like a spiritual throb that comes as near as possible to our concept of pure thought.

"This concept of the universe as a world of pure thought," says Sir James Jeans towards the close of his book, *The Mysterious Universe,* "throws a new light in many of the situations we have encountered in our survey of modern physics. We can now see how the ether, in which all events of the universe take place, could reduce to a mathematical abstraction, and become as abstract and as mathematical as parallels of latitude and meridians of longitude. We can also see why energy, the fundamental entity of the universe, had again to be treated as a mathematical abstraction—the constant of integration of a differential equation.

"The same concept implies of course that the final truth about a phenomenon resides in the mathematical description of it; so long as there is no imperfection in this, our knowledge of the phenomenon is complete. We go beyond the mathematical formula at our own risk; we may find a model or picture which helps us to understand it, but we have no right to expect this, and our failure to find such a model or picture need not indicate that either our reasoning or our knowledge is at fault. The making of models or pictures to explain mathematical formulae and the phenomena they describe, is not a step towards, but a step away from, reality; it is like making graven images of a spirit."

Professor Schroedinger himself declares emphatically that he cannot be looked upon as a pioneer in the line of thought thus expressed by Sir James Jeans. Perhaps he is not conscious of it. But the fact remains that the actual work which he has achieved must be looked upon as having a fundamental influence on this particular phase of modern physics. And it is in this perspective that it must be viewed in relation to the cultural trend of our time.

SCIENCE
THEORY
AND
MAN

I

SCIENCE, ART AND PLAY

W ITH man, as with every other species, the primary aim of thought and action is to satisfy his needs and to preserve his life. Unless the conditions of life are excessively unfavorable, there remains a surplus force; and this is true even of animals. Even with animals, this surplus manifests itself in play; an animal when playing is conscious of the fact that its activity is not directed towards any aim or towards the satisfaction of the needs of life. A ball of wool interests and amuses the kitten, but it does not hope to find any hidden dainty within. The dog continues to roll the beslavered stone and his eyes implore us to throw it again: "Put an aim before me; I have none and would like to have one." With man the same surplus of force produces an intellectual play by the side of the physical play or sport. Instances of such intellectual play are games in the ordinary sense, like card games, board games, dominoes, or riddles, and I should also count among them every kind of intellectual activity as well as Science;[1]—and if not the whole of Science at any rate the advance guard of Science, by which I mean research work proper.

Play, art and science are the spheres of human activity where action and aim are not as a rule determined by the aims imposed by the necessities of life; and even in the exceptional instances where this is the case, the creative artist or the investigating scientist soon forget this fact—as indeed they must forget it if their work is to prosper. Generally, however, the aims are chosen freely by the artist or student himself, and are superfluous; it would cause no immediate harm if these aims were not pursued. What is operating here is a surplus force remaining at our

---

[1] The word "science" is here usually the translation of *Wissenschaft*, which includes literature, archeology, philology, history, etc.

disposal beyond the bare struggle for existence: art and science are thus luxuries like sport and play, a view more acceptable to the beliefs of former centuries than to the present age. It was a privilege of princes and flourishing republics to draw artists and scientists within their sphere, and to give them a living in exchange for an activity which yielded nothing save entertainment, interest and repute for the prince or the city. In every age such procedure has been regarded as a manifestation of internal strength and health, and the rulers and peoples have been envied who could afford to indulge in this noble luxury, this source of pure and lofty pleasure.

If this view is accepted we are compelled to see the chief and lofty aim of science to-day, as in every other age, in the fact that it enhances the general joy of living. It is the duty of a teacher of science to impart to his listeners knowledge which will prove useful in their professions; but it should also be his intense desire to do it in such a way as to cause them pleasure. It should cause him at least as much satisfaction to speak before an audience of working men who have taken an hour off their leisure time in the hope of obtaining an intellectual joy as to speak before the engineers of an industrial undertaking who may be supposed to be chiefly concerned with the practical exploitation of the most recent results of scientific investigation. I need not here speak of the quality of the pleasures derived from pure knowledge; those who have experienced it will know that it contains a strong esthetic element and is closely related to that derived from the contemplation of a work of art. Those who have never experienced it cannot understand it; but that is no reason why they should "withdraw weeping from our community," since it may be supposed that they find compensation elsewhere within the sphere of art—as, for example, in the free and vigorous exercise of a well-trained body in sport, play or dance. Speaking generally, we may say that all this belongs to the same category—to the free unfolding of noble powers which remain available, beyond purely utilitarian activities, to cause pleasure to the individual and to others.

It might be objected that after all there is a considerable difference between scientific and artistic and even more between scientific and playful activity, the difference residing in the fact that scientific activity has a powerful influence on the practical shaping of life and the satisfaction of its needs. It might be said that it had eminently contributed to material well-

being and that the doctor's and the engineer's skill and
the judge's and statesman's wisdom are the fruit it
bears; and it may be urged that, on a serious view,
these fruits in which the whole of mankind can share
are of a higher value than the pleasures of study and
discovery, which are open to a few privileged men
and their listeners and readers. It might, on the other
hand, be felt that the equation of these pleasures
with art is slightly arrogant. Moreover, are we seriously to regard the practical results of science as the
acceptable by-products of learned leisure? Should
not rather the joys of research be regarded as the
pleasant accompaniment of a work which in itself, so
far from being playful, is entirely grave and devoted
to practical aims?

Judgments of value are problematical. There can
be no discussion as to the thanks due by mankind to
modern surgery, and to the men who have combated
epidemic diseases. Yet it should not be forgotten that
the advances of surgery were an antidote desperately
needed against the advances of applied science, which
would be almost unbearable without the relief provided by the surgeon's ready hand. I do not wish to
speak ill of the advances of applied science; indeed
it seems to me that one of the chief claims to fame

31

of modern applied science is that it disregards material welfare and personal security and promotes and even creates purely intellectual values which exist for their own sake and not for any given material purpose. I have here in mind chiefly, because this seems to me to be the most important point, the overcoming of distances in order to promote communication and understanding. I admit that this overcoming of distances has its material aspects. A merchant in Hamburg can reach New York in four days; he learns the exchange quotations daily on board by wireless, can give instructions to his office, and so on. But are we, mankind in general, really interested so very much in the rapidity of business transactions? I venture to deny it. What we really have at heart is something very different. What really gives us pleasure is something very different: far more people than formerly can visit different countries; the nations are brought nearer to each other, can appreciate each other's civilizations, and learn to understand each other. Daring men can penetrate into the polar ice without our being compelled to feel anxiety during months and years; for we receive signals from them, we know where they are, and we can render them assistance. Last, not least, the pure technical pleasure

32

of overcoming difficulties, the pleasure of succeeding, apart from practical advantages, is continually winning a greater place, not only in the minds of those immediately concerned, for these probably experienced it at all times, but also in the minds of entire peoples. The Zeppelin and the Blue Ribbon of the Atlantic obtained for Germany a reputation kindred to that obtained by Walther, Tasso, and Ariosto for the courts where they wrote their poetry.

These and similar considerations lead to the conviction that science with all its consequences is not such a desperately serious affair and that, all things considered, it contributes less to material well-being than is generally assumed, while it contributes more than is generally assumed to purely ideal pleasures. True, its effect on the multitude is generally indirect and the occasions are rare when science can give joy to the many by laying before it its immediate results: indeed, this happens only in those cases where it lays before the community a work of art. At any rate those who have stood with bated breath and trembling knees before the two thousand years' old dream of beauty created of white marble which the industry of archeologists has erected in the Berlin Museum will consider that at least as far as the science of archeology is concerned the question as to why it is being pursued has been answered. As a rule the way to the masses is long and less direct and in certain rare cases it may appear as though a complete barrier existed. However, we would ask that the right to exist should be acknowledged even for these distant blossoms on the Tree of Knowledge; our reason being that they must first fertilize each other in order that other branches shall be able to bear such obvious fruits, palpable to the entire community, as the Graf Zeppelin[1] or the Pergamon Altar.

From a certain standpoint, indeed, the number of individuals sharing in a given cultural achievement is really irrelevant. The truth is that arithmetic cannot be applied to matters of the mind any more than to any other manifestation of life: multiplication here becomes impossible. Once a thought has flashed in the thinker's brain it is in existence and is not increased in value by the fact that a hundred other brains follow it. This argument is correct; yet the fact must be remembered that we are not dealing with a single

---

[1] AUTHOR'S NOTE: Had this array been primarily written for English readers, another example would very probably have been chosen instead of the "Zep." But since it stands, let us take it at the same time as an impressive instance of how the latest and most outstanding achievements of science often fail to augment material welfare!

achievement of civilization or a single sphere of ideas, but with a multiplicity; and for this reason it is desirable even from the purely esoteric and scientific point of view that the approaches to these intellectual treasures should be facilitated and thrown open to the greatest possible number of persons, even if they partake of them less completely than the "initiated." In this manner there is an increasing chance that a number of cultural values may become the property, in favorable circumstances, of one individual; and this amounts to a real "multiplication" of cultural values, and indeed to more than that. When thoughts fructify they lead to new and undreamed of developments.

*

IT is sometimes said that physics is to-day in a stage of transformation and revolution; a stage described by some as a crisis. Such a stage is one of abnormal activity and of enhanced vital power. Linguistically the expression "crisis" (the Greek κρίσις equals "decision") is appropriate; yet it is misleading if it suggests anything resembling a crisis in a business undertaking, a cabinet, or in the course of a disease. In these cases we are thinking of a dangerous stage of decision followed by complete collapse; whereas in science we mean that new facts or ideas have occurred which compel us to take up a definite position in questions which had hitherto been open or, more frequently, had never passed beyond a kind of vague awareness. It is precisely our desire to be compelled to take up a definitive position; and in the exact sciences such a compulsion is frequently enough brought about deliberately by so-called crucial experiments. The more important the issue happens to be, the "worse" the "crisis" will be; and the more certainly will it lead to an extension and illumination of our scientific knowledge. I admit that the critical stage itself bears a certain similarity to the feverish stages of an illness, which is due to the sudden upsetting of opinions which had hitherto been regarded as secure; a learned delirium is no rarity. But the comparison is invalid unless we add that in the case of science the disease guarantees the patient a freer, happier, and more intensive life on his recovery. To infer from the crisis in individual sciences that there is such a thing as a general twilight of science is a mistake resting upon a confusion of words.

But though we have grasped that this critical stage is not abnormal, and still less is any harbinger of disaster, we are still faced by the question why it is that the transvaluation of all values, which is really a permanent phenomenon, has taken such an acute form not in one science, but in many, and perhaps in most. Such is the case in mathematics, chemistry, astronomy and psychology. Can this be an accident?

In experimental science facts of the greatest importance are rarely discovered accidentally: more frequently new ideas point the way towards them. The ideas which form the background of the individual sciences have an internal inter-connection, but they are also firmly connected with each other and with the ideas of the age in a far more primitive manner. This inter-connection consists in the simple fact that a far from negligible and steadily growing percentage of the men who devote themselves to scientific studies are also human beings who share in the general world of ideas of the age. The influence of these ideas can often be traced into unexpected ramifications. Thus some years ago astronomy was threatened with a kind of arterio-sclerosis due to the fact that no crisis was on the horizon; and it was saved from this phenomenon of old age, not so much by the perfection of its instruments and by the progress made by physics in the interpretation of astral spectra, as by a new and a wholly independent idea. It was suggested that really new discoveries could be reached not by careful study of individual stars, but by comparative statistics applied to vast groups of stars. This idea, which is so clearly connected with other tendencies of the times, has opened up vast new tracts and has extended our apprehension of space almost to infinity.

Our age is possessed by a strong urge towards the criticism of traditional customs and opinions. A new spirit is arising which is unwilling to accept anything on authority, which does not so much permit as demand independent, rational thought on every subject, and which refrains from hampering any attack based upon such thought, even though it be directed against things which formerly were considered to be sacrosanct as you please. In my opinion this spirit is the common cause underlying the crisis of every science to-day. Its results can only be advantageous: no scientific structure falls entirely into ruin: what is worth preserving preserves itself and requires no protection.

In my opinion this is true not only of science: it is of a far more universal application. There is never any need to oppose the assaults of the spirit of the age: that which is fit to live will successfully resist.

II

THE LAW OF CHANCE

THE PROBLEM OF CAUSATION IN MODERN SCIENCE

ABOUT the middle of the eighteenth century David Hume pointed out that there is no intrinsic connection between cause and effect which can be perceived and understood by the human mind. He further held that the causation of one phenomenon by another (such as the warming of the earth's surface by the rising of the sun) is not directly perceptible. We can only perceive that one phenomenon —the rising of the sun—is always followed by another phenomenon, namely, the warming of the earth's surface. It is also observed that the unfailing succession of certain events after certain others is not confined to any special range of phenomenā but is a characteristic feature of Nature. But neither the connection between a single cause and its effect, nor the universality of this connection throughout Nature, is in itself manifest or forms a necessary element in our thought.

The constancy of the laws of nature is guaranteed to us only by experience. Why then do we value this experience for any other reason than that it chronicles past events? Why do we concede to what has happened in the past a controlling influence on our expectation of what is to happen in the future? It is no answer to this question to say that this method of controlling our expectation has proved very useful up to the present, and therefore we cling to it. Such an answer is simply a begging of the question. For that is just the point: why do we expect that what has proved useful hitherto will continue to be so in future? Of course arguments *can* be advanced for adopting this attitude; but this becomes possible only when we change our standpoint. We then perceive that, since the course of events in nature has been governed by regularity up to the present, any species of animals which failed to reap the advantages of allowing their behavior and expectations to be guided by past experience, could not possibly have survived in the struggle for life, but would long ago have been eliminated by so severe a handicap. Hence the mere fact that we, human beings, have survived to raise the question, in a certain sense indicates the required answer!

Hume by no means doubted that in the external world a certain regularity prevails, the observation of which has led us to the very useful and practical concept of a necessary causal connection between one natural occurrence and another. Within the last few years, however, the objective existence of this very regularity has been questioned. The doubts arose from a branch of human study within which we should least expect them—that is to say, the exact science of physics. The basis of this skepticism is the altered viewpoint which we have been compelled to adopt. We have learned to look upon the overwhelming majority of physical and chemical processes as mass phenomena produced by an immensely large number of single individual entities which we call atoms and electrons and molecules. And we have further learned that the extraordinarily precise and exact regularity which we observe in these physical

41

and chemical processes is due to one general law which can be stated thus: In every physical and chemical process there is a transition from relatively well-ordered conditions among the groups of atoms and molecules to less orderly conditions—in other words, a transition from order to disorder, just as might be expected if each individual member of the mass followed its own way more or less without any plan and under no definite law. The exact laws which we observe are "statistical laws." In each mass phenomenon these laws appear all the more clearly, the greater the number of individuals that coöperate in the phenomenon. And the statistical laws are even more clearly manifested when the behavior of each individual entity is *not* strictly determined, but conditioned only by chance. It is quite understandable under such circumstances that a steady transition from regularity to irregularity must result, as a governing Law and as a general basal characteristic of all natural processes. In physics this is believed to be the source from which the very definite one-directional tendency of all natural happenings arises. If an initial state, which may be called the cause, entails a subsequent state, which may be called its effect, the latter, according to the teaching of molecular physics, is always the more haphazard or less orderly one. It is, moreover, precisely the state which can be anticipated with overwhelming probability provided it is admitted that the behavior of the single molecule is absolutely haphazard. And so we have the paradox that, from the point of view of the physicist, chance lies at the root of causality.

I shall now bring forward some examples from every-day life to illustrate how the play of pure chance can result in predictable consequences. Let us take, for instance, a huge library which is visited by thousands of curious people day after day and where all the books are in their regular places on the shelves on the Monday morning when the visitors enter. We shall imagine that these visitors are an unruly pack, badly brought up, and that they have come to sample the books in the library merely out of vulgar curiosity. Let us suppose that whenever they have taken a book from its position on the shelves they never trouble to put it back where it should be placed but replace it quite at random. The general result will be that the library will be submitted to a definite one-directional transition from order to disorder. Now the astonishing feature is that this process proves to be subject to very definite laws, especially if we suppose

43

that the volumes are taken from the shelves in the same haphazard way as they are put back.

Let us investigate the condition of affairs after one week of this barbaric invasion. If we suppose that there were eighty volumes of Goethe's works, for instance, neatly arranged in one section of the library when the casual mob entered, and if we find that only sixty volumes are now in their places while the other twenty are scattered about here and there, then we can expect that during the second week about fifteen volumes will disappear from the row, and about eleven volumes will vanish during the third week, etc. For since we have supposed that the books are taken out quite at random, the probability that one of the remaining volumes will meet with this misfortune decreases as their number decreases. Here we have a general law arising from a mass of chaotic events. The number of volumes in their proper positions diminishes in accordance with the exponential law, or Law of Geometrical Progression, as the mathematicians call it.

We find the very same law verified in many chemical and physical processes, such as the spontaneous transformation of one element into another, in the so-called disintegration of radioactive matter. Now I am sure that in the case of the books in the library the reader will hesitate to admit that the dispersal of Goethe's works would actually follow the predicted law with any appreciable accuracy. And his hesitation is justified. In such a case as this, then, is there any justification whatever for positing any "Law"? Surely the utmost we may legitimately attempt to do is to forecast probabilities. What will actually happen depends on chance. In answer to these objections it must be observed that when we are concerned with only such a small number as eighty volumes of a work in a library, we must indeed be prepared to find that the number actually in place at any given stage will deviate appreciably from the number to be expected according to the "Law." But on the other hand, with 80,000 instead of eighty volumes (in a library containing many millions of books) the casual deviations would amount to only a much smaller fraction of the total number predicted. It is possible to calculate that owing to the myriads of atoms engaged in every physical and chemical process the purely statistical forecasts will be verified with the same degree of exactitude as is actually observed in Nature's laws. But of course they can never hold good with absolute exactitude. Now it is the greatest triumph of the statistical theory of natural law, and the most convincing argument in its favor, that in many cases, such as the radioactive transformation that I have spoken of, small and quite irregular departures from the law really *are* observed. And they have proved to be of just the type and magnitude which the statistical theory had previously calculated.

As a further example of how orderliness springs from chance, we may take the case of insurance companies. The eventualities against which we are insured—accident, death, fire, burglary—depend on a thousand chances. But to the insurance company it makes no difference which of the insured buildings will be burned during the coming year or which of the insured persons will meet with an accident. The only consideration that matters to the company is what percentage of the insured meets with a misfortune that has to be compensated. That percentage can be anticipated from the statistics of former years. Therefore, despite the impossibility of foretelling the fate of any given person, the company may safely undertake, for a relatively small premium, to cover possible damages up to a high multiple of the annual payment.

I have said the statistical theory provides an intelligible explanation of the fact that the course of natural events follows a definite direction, which cannot be reversed. The explanation consists in regarding this unidirectional tendency as a development from a better ordered to a less ordered state (in every single case) of the atomic aggregation involved. We are here concerned with a very general law, the so-called Second Law of Thermodynamics, or the Law of Entropy. We are convinced that this Law governs all physical and chemical processes, even if they result in the most intricate and tangled phenomena, such as organic life, the genesis of a complicated world of organisms from primitive beginnings, the rise and growth of human cultures. In this connection the physicist's belief in a continually increasing disorder seems somewhat paradoxical, and may easily lead to a dreadfully pessimistic misunderstanding of a thesis which actually implies nothing more than the specific meaning assigned to it by the physicist. Therefore a word of explanation will be necessary.

We do not wish to assert anything more than that the *total balance* of disorder in nature is steadily on the increase. In individual sections of the universe, or in definite material systems, the movement may very well be towards a higher degree of order, which is

47

made possible because an adequate compensation occurs in some other systems. Now according to what the physicist calls "order" the heat stored up in the sun represents a fabulous provision for order, insofar as this heat has not yet been distributed equally over the whole universe (though its definite tendency is towards that dispersion), but is for the time being concentrated within a relatively small portion of space. The radiation of heat from the sun, of which a small proportion reaches us, is the compensating process making possible the manifold forms of life and movement on the earth, which frequently present the features of increasing order. A small fraction of the tremendous dissipation suffices to maintain life on the earth by supplying the necessary amount of "order" but of course only so long as the prodigal parent, in its own frantically uneconomic way, is still able to afford the luxury of a planet which is decked out with cloud and wind and rushing rivers and foaming seas and the gorgeous finery of flora and fauna and the striving millions of mankind.

Let us return to the specific question of causality. Here we are still faced with a dilemma. *Either* one can form the opinion that the real essence, or the intrinsic constitution, of the Laws of Nature has been exhaustively discovered through the revelation of their statistical character, and that consequently the idea of a necessary causal connection between natural occurrences ought to be banished from our world picture, just as the concept of heat as a fluid disappeared from physics the moment it was discovered that heat is nothing more than a random movement of the smallest particles. We shall be especially inclined to sacrifice the causal principle if we follow Hume in recognizing that it is not a necessary feature of our thought, but only a convenient habit, generated by the observation of that regularity in the course of actual occurrences the merely statistical character of which is now clearly perceived.

If, however, we disagree with Hume and hold that the causal principle is something of an *a priori* nature, forming a necessary element in our thought, and inevitably marking every possible experience with its stamp, then we must adopt *the second alternative*, which may be expressed as follows: We shall maintain that the behavior of each atom is in every single event determined by rigid causality. And we shall even contend that strictly causal determinism of the elementary processes, although we cannot observe their details, must necessarily be admitted, in order to allow the mass phenomena, which result from their coöperation, to be treated by the methods of statistics and the probability calculus. From this viewpoint causality would lie at the basis of statistical law.

This second view is the conservative one. The former is extremely revolutionary. And the one is the direct antithesis of the other. According to the revolutionary view, undetermined chance is primary and is not further explicable. Law arises only statistically in mass phenomena owing to the coöperation of myriads of chances at play in these phenomena. According to the conservative view the compulsion of law is primary and not further explicable, whereas chance is due to the coöperation of innumerable partial causes which cannot be perceived. Therefore chance here is something subjective—only a name for our own inability to discover the detailed action of numerous small component causes.

There is scarcely any possibility of deciding this issue by experiment. For the methods of pure reasoning evidently allow us either to derive chance from law, or law from chance, whichever we prefer. Wherever we are concerned with a law-determined process forming the ultimate *recognizable* structural element in our world picture, a domain of chance behind it can be supposed to produce the law statistically, if anybody desires to suppose this. And in a similar way the champion of the causal principle is justified in thinking that any chance he observes is dependent on the action of uncontrollable changing causes which give rise to this or that effect, but always compulsorily.

The current controversy about the principle of causality is a phase in our changing intellectual outlook, which is paralleled by the problem of the true character of space and time, a question which has arisen anew as a result of Einstein's theories. The old links between philosophy and physical science, after having been temporarily frayed in many places, are being more closely renewed. The farther physical science progresses the less can it dispense with philosophical criticism. But at the same time philosophers are increasingly obliged to become intimately acquainted with the sphere of research, to which they undertake to prescribe the governing laws of knowledge.

III

INDETERMINISM IN PHYSICS[1]

T HE profound changes which the picture of the
world as presented by Physics has undergone in
recent years has brought it about that the so-called
problem of causality has come into the limelight; and
discussion of this problem, far from being confined to
technical and scientific publications, has found a place
in the daily press. I do not here wish to pre-judge the
question whether the problem discussed is in fact the
problem of causality in the philosophical sense merely

[1] Paper read before the Congress of the Society for Philosophical
Instruction, Berlin, 16th June, 1931.

by using the label of causality. This name has come to be applied to these matters, they sail under this flag, and that is why I employ the expression.

The question at issue is this: given any physical system, is it possible, at any rate in theory, to make an exact prediction of its future behavior, provided that its nature and condition at one given point of time are exactly known? It is assumed, of course, that no external and unforeseen influences act upon the system from without; but such influences can always be eliminated, at least theoretically, if all bodies, fields of force and the like capable of acting upon the system are included within it. It is assumed, in other words, that the condition of these external elements, too, is exactly known at the initial moment of time. It is possible, and indeed if we argue rigorously it is certain, that in order to do so, the system under consideration has to be extended to comprehend the entire universe. Yet it is possible to *imagine* a finite, self-contained system, and in practice this abstraction is invariably made use of whenever a law of physics is enunciated. The question therefore is whether it is possible exactly to predict the behavior of such a system provided its initial condition be exactly known.

Some fifteen years ago this was never doubted:

absolute determinism was, in a manner, the fundamental dogma of practical physics. The clearest example, which had given this direction to physics, was classical mechanics: given a system of mass points, their masses, positions and velocities at an initial point of time, and given the laws of force in accordance with which they act upon one another, it was possible to calculate in advance their movements for all future time. And when applied to the celestial bodies, this theory had been triumphantly confirmed.

To-day many physicists assert that such a strictly determinist view cannot do justice to nature, and that this applies equally whether mass points, fields of force or waves are used as the bricks from which we build our system. They make this assertion on the strength of the experimental results obtained in physics during the last thirty years—results which relate to measurements of every kind; on the strength of the long-continued failure of all attempts at comprehending satisfactorily the totality of these experiments through the medium of a deterministic model; and finally on the strength of the very creditable success which has been reached by a departure from a strict determinism.

Evidently such success and failure cannot in itself

determine so grave a question. However firmly we may be convinced that it was determinism which was the stumbling block in all the attempts that had been made hitherto, and however strongly we may believe that it is the obstacle preventing a completely satisfactory explanation of all the observed phenomena; however considerable finally the successes achieved by the employment of an undeterministic picture may be, it is unlikely that we shall ever be able to demonstrate the impossibility of finding any deterministic model of nature capable of doing justice to the facts.

The modern attempts to relinquish determinism are rendered particularly interesting by the fact that their claims with regard to the absence of determinism, far from being vague and inaccurate, are quantitatively quite definite and can be expressed in centimeters, grams and seconds. As a simple example, we may take a mass point in motion either in a state of isolation from others or as a member of a system of many mass points exerting force upon each other. The claim which is made is that its movement cannot be foretold with complete accuracy because, among other things, it would be necessary to know its position and velocity at the initial point of time; and it is claimed that it is impossible in principle to determine both

55

of these exactly. Let us assume that we have succeeded in ascertaining that the point must at any rate
be situated somewhere within a small area whose
linear dimensions I will call λ. Let us take any point

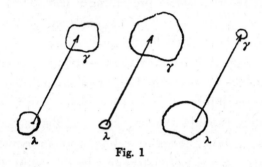

Fig. 1

within this area and from it draw an arrow to denote
velocity in the customary way. Let us next assume
that we have succeeded in determining the direction
and magnitude of the velocity sufficiently to enable
us to restrict the point of the arrow which symbolizes
these latter to a small area, whose linear dimensions
I propose to denote by γ. Finally let m denote the
mass of this material point. The sufficiently peculiar
assertion then is that the product mγλ cannot be
reduced beneath a certain definite limit. It is
claimed that the inaccuracy which is inherent in the
position (λ) and that which adheres to the velocity

56

at the same time (γ) cannot both be reduced to a greater degree, than to give the product $m\gamma\lambda$, the approximate magnitude of what is known as Planck's constant h:

$$m\gamma\lambda \text{ approximately equals } h = 6 \cdot 5 \times 10^{27} \text{ g. cm.}^2 \text{ sec.}^1$$

Now although the value of this constant is extremely small, yet it can be expressed with perfect accuracy in centimeters, grams and seconds; it can be derived from the laws governing heat radiation and by many other extremely exact methods.[1] What is claimed then is that, while it is possible to make one of the two regions (λ) and (γ) as small as may be desired, and the relative statements as exact as may be desired, this is achieved only at the cost of increasing the other. In other words, it is impossible to make both as small as may be desired (Heisenberg's relation of inexactitude). I cannot here undertake to explain in a few words the manner in which this peculiar assertion has been reached; I have quoted it merely as an example to give you a concrete instance of "indeterminism." This, however, is not all.

---

[1] In the above equation it might appear that "approximately equals h" implies that the exact value of h is irrelevant. A more exact formulation is possible if, instead of the vague idea of inaccuracy, the more precise one of mean error is used.

According to classical physics, and especially mechanics, it would be necessary to undertake certain operations in order to take a mass point to a given place at the initial point of time and in order to impress upon it a given velocity. Thus we might take it between nippers, carry it to the place in question and push it in an appropriate direction. Quantum mechanics teaches us that if such an operation is undertaken with a mass point a great number of times, the same result does not invariably come about even if the operation is always exactly the same. But it further teaches that the result obtained is not entirely a matter of chance. What is claimed is that if you repeat the same experiment a million times and register the frequency with which the different possible results occur, they will in a second million experiments repeat themselves with exactly the same frequency. It is assumed, of course, that all the experiments are exactly identical.

It will be seen that this claim approximates closely to the so-called law of trial and error governing actual measurements. What is peculiar in this theoretical assertion is the fact that there is a rigid limit to the accuracy of observation, a limit which in its turn is determined by a constant of Nature. Hitherto in all

our theoretical considerations we had quite unconsciously assumed, that at any rate in principle,
observations could be carried out with any degree
of accuracy; nobody had dreamed that a correlation
of the kind mentioned between the accuracies of the
different measurements (in the present instance position and velocity) did in fact exist.

The other assertions made by modern physics in
support of indeterminism are essentially of a similar
kind, although they are less easily comprehensible,
especially to non-physicists; and a discussion of them
would not promote our present argument. My further
observations really consist only in a number of footnotes referring to this example, but otherwise only
loosely connected with one another. A final and comprehensive judgment on these matters is at the present
moment impossible.

The first footnote refers to the relation of the new
theory to classical mechanics.

According to the new theory, identical conditions at
the beginning do not invariably lead to identical results;
all that they lead to is identical statistics (= relative frequency of the various possible events); indeed
this is precisely what we mean by indeterminateness.

Now what I wish to claim is that from a purely

59

naïve point of view classical mechanics itself is un-
determinate. The opposite is generally asserted; but
this is due merely to a technique to which we have
grown so accustomed in course of time that we take it
for granted.

Let us take a mass point in motion. We find that at
a certain moment it is at a given point; we are perfectly acquainted with the nature and condition of its
entire environment: thus, for example, in the case of a
stone which has been thrown and is situated in a gravitational field, we know all the forces acting upon it.
In such circumstances, can we tell on the lines of
classical mechanics how the body will be moving in
the next instant of time? And if the experiment is re-
peated and we find the same body in the same surroundings and at exactly the same place, will the
identical circumstances at the beginning be followed
invariably by an identical trajectory?

We know that such is not the case; we know, on the
contrary, that the mere notion of its position and of
the forces acting on the body in one moment, leaves us
in the completest ignorance of what is going to happen in the *next* moment. It is only when we *know* what
it will be doing at the *next* moment that we can make
precise predictions relating to the "next but one" (as

it were) and to all the following: for, according to classical mechanics, it is accelerations and not velocities that the bodies determine in each other.

A good deal of time had to elapse before this fact was grasped: the ancient Greeks and, as I believe, the Middle Ages up to and including Descartes were of a different opinion. Aristotle held that a central body impressed upon its satellites a uniform circular motion, and it was Galileo and Newton who realized that, while their velocities remained undetermined, it was their acceleration which was determined. If the question is asked how a mass point will be moving in the next moment the only answer furnished by classical mechanics is: "I do not know; if you want to know, watch it!"

Now the special technique by which classical mechanics dodges the awkward fact of indeterminateness (the fact that equal initial conditions are followed by different consequences) consists in including the initial velocity within the initial conditions. It simply states that the initial velocity must be given because unless it is given we are not fully acquainted with the initial condition: the initial velocity is taken as forming part of the initial condition at any given moment. Now if we look at the matter carefully it will appear very dubious whether such a procedure is permissible. Velocity, after all, is defined as a differential quotient with respect to time:

$$\frac{dx}{dt} = \text{the limit of} \frac{x_2 - x_1}{t_2 - t_1} \text{ for } t_2 - t_1 \rightarrow 0.$$

This definition refers to two moments of time and not to the state at one moment. True, it is believed that these two moments can at will be taken so close to each other as to make them "coincide" in the limit. Possibly, however, this is incorrect; possibly this mathematical process of approach to the limit, which was specially invented by Newton for mechanical purposes, is inadmissible. It may be that the mathematical apparatus devised by Newton is inadequately adapted to nature;

Fig. 2

and the modern claim that the concept of velocity becomes meaningless for a precisely defined position in space points strongly in that direction.

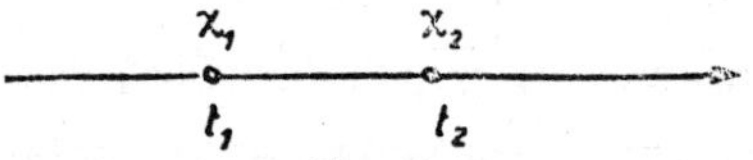

So much for the first footnote which I wish to make.

In order to avoid misunderstanding I would like to state that the above is a consideration which I have added as an afterthought to the indeterminism which has arisen in modern theory. It is not the case that the modern view is a natural growth arising out of a hypercritical scrutiny of Newton's differential calculus; if it had been possible to deal adequately with actually observed phenomena by means of Newtonian mechanics, no physicist would have found any fault with them.

My second footnote is of a somewhat different kind. Here it is necessary to make some preliminary remarks.

Presumably I may take it as known that some fifty years ago it was grasped that a very large number of so-called natural laws were statistical laws which were fulfilled with extreme accuracy only because the number of individual entities concerned was extremely great. Thus, for example, the pressure exerted by a gas on the walls of the container is taken to be the resultant of a very large number of individual impulses exerted by molecules striking against the container and rebounding from it. Now the kinetic energy of an individual molecule at a given temperature is far from being exactly determined; all that is determined is its average value, while the individual values vary somewhat considerably (their law of distribution being exactly known both theoretically and experimentally). The direction in which the molecules strike the container is wholly contingent and the number of molecules striking it in any unit of time is also, of course, subject to variations. Nevertheless, the average value of the pressure is a well-defined physical quantity. Its casual fluctuations are far beyond the limit of experimental accuracy, provided that the surface of the body, which experiences the pressure, and the time which is physically involved in the "process of averaging" is not too small. If, however, a very light and small body is subjected to pressure these conditions are not fulfilled and, as might have been expected, the purely contingent variations in pressure cause it to execute a trembling motion known as Brownian movement.

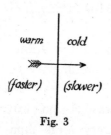

Fig. 3

But not only the laws governing the stationary equilibria have disclosed their statistical nature: the same holds, in most cases, for the dynamic evolution of physical happening. To put it briefly, all the laws relating to irreversible natural processes are now known definitely to be of a statistical kind; and this means, of course, the great majority of laws, since in the main the course of events in nature *is* irreversible. As an example I may quote the conduction of heat in a gas. An arbitrary distribution of temperature gradually approaches uniformity in a definite manner, governed by the law that the current of heat runs in the direction of the steepest fall of temperature and is proportional to the thermal gradient. To explain this on a statistical basis, let us imagine a surface within a gas, its left-hand side being warm and its right-hand side relatively cold; in other words, having relatively fast and slow-moving molecules on its left and right-hand side respectively. In accordance with the calculus of probability, approximately equal numbers of molecules will move from left to right and from right to left. The former, however, transport more energy than the latter, with the result that the thermal current flows in the direction of the gradient. The degree of exactness with which the law is fulfilled is once again due to the great number of molecules concerned. Theoretically, indeed, it would be easy to imagine cases in which the exact opposite would arise. In order to construct such a case, let us imagine that the process towards the thermal equilibrium has been going on for some time; and let us now assume that by some conjuring trick all the various velocities were exactly reversed:

this conjuring trick would leave the distribution of temperature unaltered and would produce a perfectly possible state of the system. But from *this* initial state onwards the differences in temperature would be increased through the action of thermal currents *opposed* to the fall of temperature until finally the original initial stage would be reached. Fortunately it can be shown by calculation that such a happening is unlikely in the extreme.

Since the time of Ludwig Boltzmann this view has come to be applied to the vast majority of the laws determining the events in our organic and our inorganic surroundings. All chemical transformations, the velocity of chemical reactions and their variation according to temperature, the processes of melting and evaporation, the laws of vapor pressure, etc., everything, in fact, with the possible exception of gravitation, is governed by laws of this kind, and all the "predictions" derived from these laws are of a statistical nature and are true only within limits, although these limits can be determined with complete accuracy.

Now surely we have here a striking resemblance to the modern statements concerning "indeterminateness," and it may be worth while asking why similar statements made at that earlier time did not cause quite the same degree of excitement (though they did evoke quite a little stir!) Why did nobody say, forty or fifty years ago, that modern physics (modern as it was then) was compelled to give up causality and determinism? Why was this sort of thing being said only five or six years ago?

The answer is easy. At that time the negation of determinism would have been a practical negation: to-day it is supposed to be a theoretical one. Fifty years ago it was held that, if the position and velocity of every molecule was completely known at the beginning, and if the trouble were taken to make an exact mathematical calculation of all the collisions between the molecules, then it would be possible to predict exactly what would happen. It was believed that what forced us to content ourselves with average laws was merely the practical impossibility (1) of finding out exactly what was the initial condition of the molecules and (2) of pursuing the fate of the molecules with complete mathematical accuracy. Nor was any regret felt at this confinement to average laws, because average values were all that our crude senses enabled us to observe; therefore the laws calculated on this basis proved sufficiently accurate to predict our observations with all desirable precision.

To sum up: it was held that the individual atoms and molecules were subject to a rigid determinism which formed a kind of background to those statistical mass laws which in practice were alone available empirically. And the majority of physicists considered this deterministic background to be a most essential foundation for the physical universe. They considered it a logical contradiction to surrender such a belief, and held it necessary to assume that in such an elementary event as the collision of two atoms, the result was predetermined by the preceding conditions fully and with complete accuracy. It was said (and continues to be said) that an exact knowledge of nature is impossible on any other basis, that all the foundations would be lost, that without a determinist background our view of nature would become wholly chaotic and that accordingly it would not fit the nature actually given to us, since this nature is not a complete chaos.

Now this view is certainly erroneous. It is quite certain that the view of the events within a gas as held by the kinetic theory of gases may be modified to the effect that the future trajectory of two molecules, after they have collided, is determined, not by the well-known laws of impact, but by an appropriate law of chance. All we have to do is to see that the laws of chance which we admit should, with reasonable accuracy, take care of certain "bookkeeping" laws (or "laws of conservation," to use the technical term); e.g., that the sum of the energies before and after the collision shall be approximately the same. For this much has been empirically demonstrated even for individual molecules. These bookkeeping laws do not, however, determine the result of the collision unequivocally: and it might be the case that, apart from them, there predominated a "prior" contingency. For this would not introduce a further degree of uncertainty into the result of the collision than there already is from the determinist view. We do not know whether, e.g. in the case of a given collision, the one molecule hits the other a little further to the right or to the left, which affects the result of the collision immensely (though not the conservation laws, of course). Whether we regard the result of the collision as being determined by this "a little further to the right or left" or whether we regard it as primarily undetermined (the "conservation laws" at the same time remaining unaffected) is a matter of indifference.

Fifty years ago it was simply a matter of taste or philosophic prejudice whether the preference was given to determinism or indeterminism. The former was favored by ancient custom, or possibly by an *a priori* belief. In favor of the latter it could be urged that this ancient habit demonstrably rested on the actual laws which we observe functioning in our surroundings. As soon, however, as the great majority or possibly all of these laws are seen to be of a statistical nature, they cease to provide a rational argument for the retention of determinism.

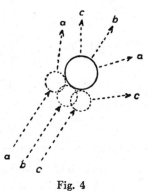

Fig. 4

We may briefly summarize this second footnote as follows: Long before modern quantum mechanics made its quantitative statements with respect to the degree of inaccuracy, it was possible, although it was not necessary, to doubt the justification of determinism from a far more general point of view. In fact,

70

such doubts were raised in 1918 by Franz Exner, nine years before Heisenberg set up his relation of indeterminacy. Little attention was paid to them, however, and if support was given to them, as by the author in his inaugural dissertation at Zurich,[1] they met with considerable shaking of heads.

So much for the second footnote. In turning to the third footnote we reach a very different group of considerations.

Let us begin by reverting to the indeterminacy which quantum mechanics predicates of the material point (see remarks on Fig. 1). On a little reflection it will be clear that the object referred to by quantum mechanics in this connection is not a material point in the old sense of the word. A material point in that sense is a thing situated at a given place, whether this place is discovered or not. And if it has a given place at any given moment then surely it must have a definite trajectory, and also, as might be assumed, at any rate at first sight, a definite velocity. However this may be, quantum mechanics forbids the conception of a well determined trajectory. It is admitted merely as a large scale approximation; after all, we can photo-

---

[1] *Die Naturwissenschaften* 17-9-1929 (delivered 1922). See Chapter VI of this book.

graph the trajectory even of atoms (the Wilson chamber cloud track). But on a microscopic scale—e.g. to the electron within the atom—the conception has to be abandoned. We have ceased to believe in the circular and elliptical orbits within the atom. To speak of electrons and protons as material points and yet to deny that they have definite orbits appears to be both contradictory and absurd. Again it should neither be disputed nor passed over in tactful silence (as is done in certain quarters) that the concept of the material point undergoes a considerable change which as yet we fail thoroughly to understand.

On the other hand the atomistic point of view itself can afford an understanding or at least raise the suspicion that the concept of the orbit should be lost when we deal with extremely small dimensions. To explain this we must, however, begin with the phenomenology of the matter—with the manner in which we actually observe the phenomena and with the aids theoretically available for that purpose.

I propose to begin with the assertion that every quantitative observation, every observation making use of measurement, is, by its nature, discontinuous.

To take the simplest possible example—that of measuring a length. For the purpose we use a rod divided into millimeters, and we find a length of 23, 24 or 25 millimeters as the case may be: our instrument gives us nothing intermediate. However, we may be able to estimate tenths of a millimeter or we may use a vernier which may give us 23.6 or 23.7 or 23.8; but again we can get nothing intermediate. With practice we may be able to guess half vernier divisions; but even then all we can obtain is a series of figures with intervals between them—23.6, 23.65, 23.7, 23.75, etc. And however far we go in the pursuit of accuracy we shall never get anything other than a finite series of discrete results which are *a priori* settled by the nature of the instrument.

In principle this is the case with every measurement; every measurement is an interrogation of nature and it is we who have arranged in advance a finite number of replies, while nature is always in the position of a voter in a ballot, with the difference that in the majority of cases nature is not given two balls, one black, one white, but a green and a yellow as well; indeed, the number may be 20, or even 10,000: but it is always a finite number. Nature never is in the position of a man filling in a voting paper on which he can write what he likes.

The instance of measuring a length may appear

somewhat trivial; yet if we consider the case in its universal application we must admit that the manner in which we obtain our quantitative knowledge of nature (the only manner in which we can obtain it), is rather primitive. The result will largely depend on the order in which we put our questions.[1] If we want to we can reduce the questions to a series to be answered by either yes or no, as in the well-known parlor game.

Fig. 5

It follows that the raw material of our quantitative cognition of nature will always have this primitive and discontinuous character. We decline to remain satisfied with it and we supplement it. Our chief aid to this end is interpolation. We rightly consider it more or less a matter of contingency if our measuring rod happens to allow us to read nothing below millimeters and our watch nothing below fifths of a second. Let us assume that we are attempting in this way

[1] Our "contact" with nature evidently is relatively loose; yet it is the best available in the form of existence which, *faute de mieux*, may be called the "present" (although if there are other forms the concept of time would probably not be common to all).

74

to determine the trajectory of a stone and have determined its coordinates to the nearest millimeter at every fifth of a second. We interpolate the intermediate points and thus reach the concept of a continuous trajectory—a trajectory, however, which itself has not been the subject of immediate quantitative observation.

What right have we thus to practice interpolation? Our justification consists in the fact that we rightly assume that we *might* employ a different method of measurement and *could* observe the position at any intermediate stage and with greater exactness.

The question now arises whether this method of interpolation is really valid: we must ask whether the concept of the continuous trajectory—which is posterior to this method—is being subjected to abuse if we believe that it must inevitably be applicable to spaces and periods of time, however small. Interpolation is justified whenever we have a right to assume that measurements made at a number of intermediate points are capable of being undertaken in principle; and when this is the case, interpolation always has a meaning and is always justified. Now, when we are dealing with the movement of an electron within an atom, it is subject to the gravest doubt whether a number of measurements along its orbit can be imagined as capable of being undertaken even in principle, the aim being that the coördinated spatial and temporal measurements should be exact enough to allow at least the rough construction of an orbit by interpolation. For such a purpose our yard-sticks would have to be constructed of "ultra-matter" and not of common atoms and molecules: these would be far too coarse. We would require watches making ten or twenty ticks in the time of a single revolution; and it must probably be regarded as a matter, not of contingency, but as an essential feature of the physical world, that such instruments are not available.

Accordingly when we speak of such trajectories we must not forget that they go beyond that which can actually be observed and that the observed has been supplemented by fictitious observations of which it is practically certain that they cannot be carried through in reality. I would not go so far as to say that an attempt in that direction would be a contradiction in terms, leading inevitably to difficulties; in the first instance, at any rate, it might have been considered permissible to complete the picture presented by nature by measurements with watches and instruments of optimum accuracy, even if in fact these watches and instruments do not exist: for after all, we are bound to supplement our immediate observations, in order not to be left with a patchwork of individual facts instead of reaching some sort of "Weltbild." Again, certain of the complements which we cannot avoid making are of the kind which relate to facts incapable of observation in principle. Among these we may perhaps count the simple fact that we are convinced of the three-dimensional nature of objects although the image on the retina is two-dimensional; we are convinced that the two fronts of the Marble Arch exist simultaneously although at any one moment we can see only one or the other.

However that may be, in the present case the *possibility* remains that the complements we interpolate are a mistake and serve merely to confuse our idea of nature. To avoid misunderstanding I would add that I am not speaking of the comparatively simple possibility that we may be mistaken in the form of the orbit and that we may take ellipses for circles or some more complicated curves for ellipses. Philosophically this possibility is wholly uninteresting. My point is that it may be possible that the very ideas of position and trajectory may be seen to be inapplicable, when used with reference to such extremely small spatial and temporal dimensions.

This is the present-day attitude of physics: ti ie will show whether it is right or wrong.

I should like finally to revert to our original question of determinism as against indeterminism. The question was whether, given complete knowledge of the state of an isolated system, it is possible to predict its future behavior accurately and unequivocally. Is nature of such a kind that this might be possible, at any rate theoretically, even if we are practically unable to obtain the necessary data?

Let us now consider the question from the phenomenological standpoint previously mentioned. From this point of view the number of answers possible to any question addressed to nature must be finite: in fact we may safely say that there can only be two answers, yes or no. If there are more they can be analyzed into a series of consecutive questions. Now in practice we can inform ourselves on the condition of a system at any given moment only by a number of individual observations: in principle any other method is impossible. And if we have made a merely finite number of observations our information on the initial state must consist in a finite series of ayes and noes. In writing, the series might be expressed as a succession of 0's and 1's.

001011110 . . . 0110100001

It is possible that a physical system might be so
simple that this meager information would suffice to
settle its fate: in that case nature would not be more
complicated than a game of chess. To determine the
positions in a game of chess, thirty-three facts suffice.
If I know of every piece where it is or whether it has
been taken, and if I know whose move it is, then I know
the position of the game, and a super-player would be
able to state definitely whether White could force a
win by playing correctly or whether he could only
force a draw or whether, if Black plays correctly,
White must lose.

If nature is more complicated than a game of chess,
a belief to which one tends to incline, then a physical system cannot be determined by a finite number
of observations. But in practice a finite number of
observations is all that we can make. All that is left
to determinism is to believe that an infinite accumula-
tion of observations would in principle enable it
completely to determine the system. Such was the
standpoint and view of classical physics, which latter
certainly had a right to see what it could make of it.
But the opposite standpoint has an equal justification:

79

we are not compelled to assume that an infinite number of observations, which cannot in any case be carried out in practice, would suffice to give us a complete determination.

This is the direction in which modern physics has led us without really intending it.

IV

IS SCIENCE A FASHION
OF THE TIMES?[1]

THERE is a well-known saying of Zola's, that art
is nature seen through the medium of a temperament—*L'art c'est la nature vue au travers d'un
tempérament.* Can the same be said of science? The
question is an important one, because it affects a
fundamental claim which is nowadays frequently put
forward in the name of science. Unlike painting and
literature and music, which are subjective ways of

---

[1] Expanded from an Address to the Physics and Mathematics
Section of the Prussian Academy of Science, February 18, 1932, and
freely rendered by Dr. James Murphy.

apprehending reality and, therefore, liable to alter with the alteration of the cultural environment, science is said to furnish us with a body of truth which has not been molded by the human temperament, and is accordingly objective and stable. How far is this true?

Before answering the question directly it will be necessary to make a distinction between two groups of sciences. On the one hand we have what are called the "exact" sciences and, on the other, those that deal with the human spirit and its activities. To the latter group belong such sciences as history, sociology, psychology, etc.

Now it is obvious, I think, that the body of truth which these humanist sciences put forward cannot claim to be entirely objective. Let us take history as an instance. Although we demand of the historian that he will keep to the objective truth of the events he describes, yet if he is to be something more than a mere chronicler, his work must go beyond the discovery and narration of bald fact. Therefore, the selection which he makes from the raw material at his disposal, his formulation of it, and his final presentation must necessarily be influenced by his whole personality. And indeed we gladly forgive the subjective intrusion of the historian into the material he is dealing with, provided we feel the touch of a strong personality weaving for us an interesting human pattern from the bald events of history. Indeed, it is here that scientific history begins, while the work of the conscientious chronicler is looked upon as merely furnishing its raw material.

Similar remarks apply to all those sciences that deal with human life and conduct. One and all, the presentation of their truths must necessarily show the active influence of the human temperament. Of course there is always the ideal of maintaining the greatest possible degree of objectivity in the procedure of these sciences, and a work in this branch of study will be considered scientific or otherwise insofar as it remains faithful to or falls away from the objective ideal. Yet there is not one of those humanist sciences that has not a certain artistic element in it. And in so far as they have this they come under Zola's description. The object with which they deal is always *vue au travers d'un tempérament.*

Let us now turn to the "exact" sciences. From the procedure followed in these sciences everything subjective is excluded on principle. Physical Science belongs essentially to this category. From all physical research the subjective intrusion of the researcher is rigorously barred so that the purely objective truth about inanimate nature may be arrived at. Once this truth is finally stated it can be put to the test of experiment by anybody and everybody all the world over, and always with the same result. Thus far Physics is entirely independent of the human temperament, and this is put forward as its chief claim to acceptance. Some of the champions of Physical Science go so far as to postulate that not only must the individual human mind be ruled out in the ultimate statements of physical research, but that the human aspect as a whole must also be excluded. Every degree of anthropomorphism is rigorously shut out; so that at least in this branch of science man would no longer be the measure of all things, as the Greek Sophists used to maintain.

Is that claim entirely true? To a greater degree than in the case of any other science it is true. But I think it goes too far. We may readily grant that a physical experiment, say, for simplicity's sake, a counting of stars, is independent of the question whether it is carried out by Mr. Wilson in New York or Fräulein Mueller in Berlin. The result will always be the same, provided of course that the requisite technical conditions are fulfilled.

The same is true of all established experiments in Physics. The first and indispensable condition that we demand of any process of experiment before it can be admitted into the regular procedure of physical research is that it will invariably reproduce the same results. We do not consider an experiment worthy of scientific consideration or acceptance unless it can fulfill this condition. Now, it is from the immense mass of individual results accruing from such reproducible experiments that the whole texture of Physical Science is woven. And these classical results are the only raw material allowed to be used in the further development of scientific truth. Therefore, as no other source of knowledge than that of exact experiment is admitted here, it would seem at first sight that Physical Science is wholly within its rights in putting forward its claim to be the authentic bearer of absolutely objective truth. But in estimating that claim certain further considerations must be taken into account.

The legitimate data of Physical Science are always and exclusively those arrived at by means of experiment. But consider the number of experiments which have actually furnished the data on which the structure of Physical Science is based. That number is undoubtedly very large. But it is infinitesimal when compared with the number of experiments that might have been carried out, but never actually have been. Therefore, a selection has been made in choosing the raw material on which the present structure of science is built. That selection must have been influenced by circumstances that are other than purely scientific. And thus far Physical Science cannot claim to be absolutely independent of its environment.

Let us take some of the factors that come into play when a selection has to be made from the experiments that offer themselves as possibilities if somebody wishes to undertake a work of research in some new direction. Obviously there is first and foremost the question of what experiments are practical in the circumstances. Certain experiments demand complicated and expensive apparatus, and the means of securing these are not always at hand. No matter how promising these experiments may be, they have to be set aside by reason of the high expense which they would entail.

Another group of possible experiments is set aside for entirely different and more subjective reasons. They suggest themselves to the mind of the scientist, but for the moment he finds them uninteresting, not only because they are not related directly to the undertaking that he has on hand but also because he may think he already knows the results to which they would lead. And even if he feels that he cannot exactly forecast such results, he may find them of secondary importance at the moment and thus neglect them. Moreover, there is the consideration that if he were to take all such results into consideration he would not know what to do with their immense number. Add to this the fact that our minds are not of infinite compass in their range of interests. Certain things absorb our attention for the moment. The result is that there must always be a large number of alternative experiments—and very practical experiments too—which we do not think of at all, simply because our interest is attracted in other directions.

All this leads to the inevitable conclusion that we cannot close the door to the entry of subjective factors in determining our scientific policy and in giving a definite direction to our line of further advance.

Of course it goes without saying that any advance which we undertake is immediately dependent on the data here and now at our disposal. And these data represent results that have been achieved by former researchers. These results are the outcome of selections formerly made. Those selections were due to a certain train of thought working on the mass of experimental data *then* at hand. And so if we go back through an indefinite series of stages in scientific advance, we shall finally come to the first conscious attempt of primitive man to understand and form a logical mental picture of events observed in the world around him.

These first observations of nature by primitive man did not arise from any consciously constructed mental pattern. The image of nature which primitive man formed for himself emerged automatically, as it were, from the surrounding conditions, being determined by the biological situation, the necessity of bodily sustenance within the environment, and the whole interplay between bodily life and its vicissitudes on the one hand and the natural environment on the other. I mention this point in order to forestall the objection that from the very start a compulsory element might be attributed to the overpowering sway of objective facts. This is certainly not true, the origin of science being without any doubt the very anthropomorphic necessity of man's struggle for life.

It often happens that a certain idea, or group of ideas, becomes vital and dominant at a certain juncture and illuminates with a new significance certain

lines of experiment which hitherto have been considered uninteresting and unimportant. Thirty years ago,
for instance, nobody was particularly interested in
asking how the thermal capacity of a body changes
with the temperature, and scarcely anybody dreamed
of placing any importance on the reaction of thermal
capacity to extremely low temperatures. Perhaps
some old crank, entirely devoid of ideas, might have
been interested in the question—or maybe a very
brilliant genius. But once Nernst put forward his
famous "third law of thermodynamics" the whole situation suddenly altered. The Nernst theorem not only
embodied the surprising prediction that the thermal
capacity of all bodies at an extremely low temperature would tend toward zero, but it also proved that
all chemical equilibria could be calculated in advance
if the heat of reaction at a certain temperature were
known, together with the thermal capacity of the re-
acting bodies, down to a sufficiently low temperature.

Much the same sort of thing has taken place in regard to the so-called elasticity constants. The physicist had hitherto ignored the significance of the
numerical value of these constants and left the whole
question to the interest of the practical engineer, the
bridge-builder, and the seismologist. But when Ein-

89

stein and, after him, Debye, put forward a general theory for the lowering of the thermal capacity of bodies at low grades of temperature, whereby the temperature at which the lowering of the thermal capacity first became manifest is shown to be related to the elastic properties of the material in question, this absolutely novel and unexpected connection aroused a new interest which led to widespread experimental researches in this domain, extending it, for example, to crystals in the various crystallographic directions, etc., etc.

Another instance, which now appears almost as an example of tragic neglect, is the experiment in the diffraction of light which was carried out by Grimaldi (1613-1663). This Italian scientist discovered that the shadow of a wire formed by intercepting a beam of light coming through a slit from a distant source does not show the characteristics that might have been expected; that is to say, it is not a simple dark band across a light field. The dark band is a complex affair. It is bordered by three colored stripes whose respective widths become smaller toward the outside, while the inner part of the shadow is traversed by an odd number of light-colored lines parallel to the borders of the shadow. This experiment, which was carried out long before Huygens' wave theory and Newton's corpuscular theory of light were put forward, was the first experiment of its kind to prove clearly and definitely that rays of light do not travel strictly in straight lines and that the deviation from the direct line is very closely connected with the color or, as we should say to-day, with the wave-length.

In our day this is considered a fundamental fact not only for the understanding of the propagation of light but also in our general scientific picture of the physical universe. If we were to express the significance of Grimaldi's experiment in contemporary terms, we should say that Grimaldi had made the first demonstration of that indeterminacy in Quantum mechanics which was formulated by Heisenberg in 1927. Until the time of Young and Fresnel, Grimaldi's observations attracted little or no attention and nobody attached any great importance to them. They were regarded as pointing to a phenomenon which had no general interest for science as such, and for the following one hundred and fifty years no similar experiments were carried out, though this could have been done with the simplest and cheapest material. The reason for this was that, of the two theories of light which soon afterward were put forward, Newton's corpuscular theory gained general acceptance against the wave theory of Huygens, and thus the general interest was directed along a different path. Following this path, other interesting experiments were carried out which were of practical importance and led to correct practical conclusions, such as the laws of reflection and refraction and their application to the construction of optical instruments. We have no right to-day to say that Newton's corpuscular theory was the wrong one, though it was the custom for a long time to declare it so. The latest conclusions of modern science conform neither to the corpuscular theory nor to the wave theory. According to modern scientific conclusions, the two theories throw light upon two quite different aspects of the phenomenon, and we have not been able up to the present to bring these two aspects into harmony with each other. The interest which was taken in the one side of the question for a long time absolutely submerged any interest that might have been taken in the other. Referring to the history of experimental research into the nature of light, and various theories that arose at one time or another from this research, Ernst Mach remarks "how little the development of science takes place in a logical and systematic way." A very similar—or rather the reverse—case occurred with the theories relating to the constitution of matter. In the case of matter, the corpuscular theory was the one to hold the field up to very recent days, because it is much more difficult to bring forward experimental confirmation of the wave theory in regard to matter than was the case in regard to light.

Following Kirchoff we have become accustomed to admit that science is ultimately concerned with nothing else than a precise and conscientious description of what has been perceived through the senses. The dictum of this eminent theorist has often been quoted as a prudent warning to all those who engage in the construction of theories. From the epistemological point of view it undoubtedly contains a good deal of truth; but it is not in accord with the *psychology* of research. It is completely erroneous to believe that anybody attaches any interest whatsoever to the quantitative laws that are discovered during experimental research—*if we take these laws by themselves,* such as the fact, for instance, that the vapor pressure of some organic compounds or the specific heat of the elements depends in this way or that way on temperature. Our interest in any investigation of this type is due to some further consideration which we intend to attach to the result, that we try to get hold of. And here it is immaterial whether this anticipated consideration, or line of thought, be already existent in the shape of a clearly defined and elaborate theory or whether it be still in the embryonic stage of being a mere vague intuition in the brain of some genius in experimental research.

The psychological truth of what I have said becomes manifest the moment we are faced with the difficulty of explaining to the layman just *why* one is carrying out this or that investigation. When I speak of the layman here I do not mean the term to apply just to those people who do not give their minds to the consideration of impractical things, either because they are not interested in them or because they are overwhelmed by everyday matters. I mean the term to extend much wider. In the circle of a learned society which unites representatives of the various branches of science and literature in order to coöperate in research work, every day one finds one's self a layman in the sense quoted above. Each of one's fellow-members finds himself to be a layman in the same sense. For after having attended a lecture given by a colleague he frequently cannot help asking himself (disrespectful though it may sound): what, in the name of Providence, is the fellow making such a fuss about? That attitude is of course not really meant offensively. But it is a very good illustration of the point that I am making, namely, that quite a special trend of interest is needed in order that a man may readily admit the extreme importance of some— and the unimportance of others—of the multitudinous questions that can be put to nature. In the case just mentioned (let us say it was your own lecture) it may happen that a colleague comes up to you and says: "Look here, do tell me why that particular thing interests you. To me it seems quite immaterial whether, etc., etc. ..." Then you will endeavor to explain. You will try to show all the connections your theme has with others. You will try to *defend* your own interest in the matter. I mean that you will try to defend the reason *why* you are interested. Then you will probably notice that your feelings are much more ardently aroused in this discussion than they were during the lecture itself. And you will become aware of the fact that only now, in your discussion with your colleague, have you reached those aspects of the subject that are, so to speak, nearest to your heart.

In passing, I may say that here we meet one of the

strongest arguments in favor of bringing together the representatives of the remote branches of science or of literature into associations for collaboration in research work. These associations are helpful and recuperative in compelling a man to reflect now and again on what he is doing and to give an account of his aims and motives to others whom he considers his equals in a different province of the realm of knowledge. Therefore, he will take the trouble to prepare a proper answer to their questions. For he will feel himself responsible for their lack of comprehension and will not haughtily look upon it as their fault instead of his own.

But though it be granted that the special importance of an investigation cannot of course be grasped without knowing the whole trend of research that had preceded it and had attracted attention to that particular line of experimentation, it might still be seriously questioned whether this fact really points to a highly subjective element in science. For on the other side it might be said that scientists all the world over are fairly well agreed as to what further investigations in their respective branches of study would be appreciated or not. One may reasonably ask whether that is not a proof of objectivity.

Let us be definite. The argument applies to the research workers all the world over, but only of *one* branch of science and of *one* epoch. These men practically form a unit. It is a relatively small community, though widely scattered, and modern methods of communication have knit it into one. The members read the same periodicals. They exchange ideas with one another. And the result is that there is a fairly definite agreement as to what opinions are sound on this point or that. There is professional enthusiasm about any progress that may be made, and whatever particular success may be achieved in one country, or by one man or group of men, will be hailed as a common triumph by the profession as a whole. In this respect international science is like international sport and also, as nothing immediately utilitarian is expected from either, they both belong to the higher and detached realm of human activity.

Now, the internationality of science is a very fine and inspiring thing; but it just renders this *"consensus omnium"* slightly suspicious as an argument in favor of the objectivity of science. Take the case of international sport. It is perfectly true that we have conditions which secure an objective and impartial registration of how high So-and-So jumped or how

97

far So-and-So threw the discus. But are not the high jump and the discus-throwing largely a question of fashion? And is it not the same with this or that line of experiments in physics?

In public sport we are acquainted only with certain kinds of games that have been developed, largely because of some current interest or because of racial tastes or climatic conditions; but we have no grounds for saying that these furnish a thoroughly exhaustive or objective picture of what human muscular ability is capable of. And in science we are acquainted only with a certain bulk of experimental results which is infinitesimally small compared with the results that might have been obtained from other experiments. Just as it would be useless for some athlete in the world of sport to puzzle his brain in order to initiate something new—for he would have little or no hope of being able to "put it over," as the saying is—so too it would, generally speaking, be a vain endeavor on the part of some scientist to strain his imaginative vision toward initiating a line of research hitherto not thought of. The incidents that I have already quoted from the history of science are proof of that point.

Our civilization forms an organic whole. Those

fortunate individuals who can devote their lives to the profession of scientific research are not merely botanists or physicists or chemists, as the case may be. They are men and they are children of their age. The scientist cannot shuffle off his mundane coil when he enters his laboratory or ascends the rostrum in his lecture hall. In the morning his leading interest in class or in the laboratory may be his research; but what was he doing the afternoon and evening before? He attends public meetings just as others do or he reads about them in the press. He cannot and does not wish to escape discussion of the mass of ideas that are constantly thronging into the foreground of public interest, especially in our day. Some scientists are lovers of music, some read novels and poetry, some frequent the theaters. Some will be interested in painting and sculpture. And if any one should believe that he could really escape the influence of the cinema, because he does not care for it, he is surely mistaken. For he cannot even walk along the street without paying attention to the pictures of cinema stars and advertisement tableaux. In short, we are all members of our cultural environment.

From all this it follows that the engaging of one's interest in a certain subject and in certain directions

must necessarily be influenced by the environment, or what may be called the cultural milieu or the spirit of the age in which one lives. In all branches of our civilization there is one general world outlook dominant and there are numerous lines of activity which are attractive because they are the fashion of the age, whether in politics or in art or in science. These also make themselves felt in the "exact" science of physics.

Now how can we perceive and point out such subjective influences actually at work? It is not easy to do so if we confine ourselves to the contemporary perspective; because there are no coördinates of reference within the same cultural milieu to show how far individual directions are influenced by the spirit of the milieu as a whole. At the present moment practically one culture spans the whole earth, and so the development of science and art in different countries is to a great extent influenced by one and the same general trend of the times. For that reason it is best to take historical instances to elucidate what I have said, because in the past organic cultures were confined to much smaller territories and there was a greater variety of them at the same time on this planet.

Grecian culture is a classic example of how every

line of activity within the one cultural milieu is dominated by the general trend of the culture itself. In Hellenic science and art and in the whole Hellenic outlook on life we can immediately discern a common characteristic. The clear, transparent and rigid structure of Euclidian geometry corresponds to the plain, simple, and limited forms of the Grecian temple. The whole structure of the temple is small, near at hand, completely visible within the range of the onlooker's eye, losing itself nowhere and escaping the eye nowhere either in its extension or form. This is something quite different from Gothic architecture. So, too, in the case of Greek science the idea of the infinite is scarcely understood. The concept of a limitless process frightened the Greek, as is evidenced in the well-known paradox of Achilles and the tortoise. The Hellenic mind could not have interested itself in the Dedekind definition of the irrational number, although the idea of the irrational was already present in the synoptic form of the diagonal of the square or of the cube.

Greek drama, especially that of the earlier epochs, is absolutely static when compared to ours. There is little or no action. We are presented with a tragic situation and the action is limited to the decision which a human being makes in certain definite circumstances. So also in Greek physics the dynamic is missing. The Greek did not dream of analyzing motion in its single subsequent phases, of asking at any moment for the cause of what would happen in the next moment, as Newton did. The Greek would have found this sort of analysis petty and incompatible with his esthetic sense. He thought of the path along which a body moved as a whole, not as something that develops but as something that is already there in its entirety. In looking for the *simplest* type of motion the rectilinear one was excluded because the straight line is not perceptible in its entire range—rectilinear motion is never completed, can never be grasped as a whole. By observing the star-strewn heavens the Greek was helped over his difficulty in regard to the concept of motion. He concluded from this that a circular path uniformly traversed is the most perfect and natural movement of a body, and that it is controlled and actuated in this movement by a greater central body. I do not think that we are warranted to-day in laughing at this naïve construction of the Greek mind. Until a short time ago we have been doing a very similar thing ourselves in the quantum theory of the atom. *Faute de mieux*, we have contented ourselves with similar naïvetés and the steps that we tried beyond them have emphasized rather than liquidated the fiasco of the Newtonian differential analysis.

Let me now turn to another instance. The idea of evolution has had more dominant influence than any other idea in all spheres of modern science and, indeed, of modern life as a whole, in its general form as well as in the special presentation of it by Darwin (namely, automatic adjustment by the survival of the fittest). As an indication of how profound the idea was, we may first recall to mind the fact that even such a clear-sighted intellect as that of Schopenhauer was incapable of grasping it (indeed he violently rejected it because he considered it to be in contradiction to his own, equally profound, conception that "Now" is always one and the same instant of time and that the "I" is always one and the same person) —while, on the other hand, Hegel's philosophy, by embodying that idea, has prolonged its life up to our day—far beyond its natural span. Moreover, Ernst Mach has applied it to the scientific process itself, which he looked upon as a gradual accommodation of thoughts to facts through a choice of what we find most useful to fit in with the facts and a rejection of the less appropriate. In astrophysics we have learned to look on the various types of stars as different stages in one and the same stellar evolution. And quite recently we have seen the idea put forward that perhaps the universe on the whole is not in a stationary stage, but that at a definite point of time, which is relatively not very long ago, it changed from quite a different condition into a steadily expansive stage which, according to the results of Hubble's extraordinary observations, seems to be its present stage. (These observations show that the spectral lines of very distant nebulæ are appreciably shifted to greater wave-lengths and that this displacement is proportioned to the distance of the nebulæ. This points to immensely great velocities on the part of these systems moving away from us, so that it would appear as if the whole universe is in the process of a general expansion.) We do not consider this hypothesis as mere empty phantasy, because we have grown accustomed to the evolutionary idea. If such ideas had been put forward in a former age they certainly would have been rejected as nonsensical.

All this shows how dependent science is on the fashionable frame of mind of the epoch of which it forms a part. When we are in the midst of a general situation ourselves it is difficult for us to see general resemblances. Being so near, we are apt to perceive only the marked distinctions and not to notice the likenesses. It is just as when we first see the several members of the same family one after another we readily perceive the resemblances, but if we come to know the family intimately then we see only the differences. So too when we live in the midst of a cultural epoch it is difficult to perceive the characteristics that are common to various branches of human activity within that epoch. Let us take another example to illustrate this. A German father looking at the drawings of a ten-year-old son will mark only the individual qualities and will not readily perceive the influence of a general European type of drawing and painting. But if he looks at the drawings of a young Japanese boy he will readily recognize the influence of the Japanese style as a whole. In each case the naïve attempt of the boy is controlled and molded even in its smallest detail by the artistic tradition amid which he lives.

V

PHYSICAL SCIENCE AND THE TEMPER OF THE AGE

I N this chapter I shall discuss the question of how far the picture of the physical universe as presented to us by modern science has been outlined under the influence of certain contemporary trends which are not peculiar to science at all. We find these same trends dominating our arts and crafts, our politics and our industrial and social organizations. In art, for instance, a dominant idea is that of simplicity and purposefulness—*reine Sachlichkeit*, to use a German expression—and in all our crafts the same thought rules. In politics and in the social order the desire for change and freedom from the yoke of law, convention and authority, are outstanding features. Our philosophical and ethical outlook is distinctly relative rather than absolute. In our social and commercial and industrial organizations the methods of mass control and rationalization are the vogue of the day. To these are allied that extraordinary invention of our time which goes by the name of statistics. Let us take each of these main trends and discuss it separately, pointing out similar features in contemporary physical science.

Simplicity and purposefulness in the arts and the crafts. Few portrait painters of our day—to take this one branch of art as an illustration—would think of painting a portrait like that of Raphael's Leo X, where every detail of dress and furniture is worked out with consummate care. Our artists will be satisfied to catch the main features of their sitter and they will consider all attempts at decoration or careful painting of accessories as a hindrance to the main purpose, which is to present the *character* of the sitter as expressed in its main features. Behind all our craftsmanship there is the very same will to pur-

107

posefulness. In the construction of our houses, in the manufacture of our furniture and all our domestic accessories, in the lines of construction followed by our motor car and railway and naval engineers, everything is banished which does not contribute to the main purpose in view. We feel that we do not want any ornamentation that would not be in harmony with the keynote of practical usefulness. And we banish these decorative accessories not in any spirit of philistinism or vulgar utilitarianism, but rather because we are convinced that if the criterion of usefulness be thoroughly carried out it will evolve its own type of beauty. We are no longer afraid of broad empty spaces in our furniture or on our walls. We haven't what the Germans call *Platzangst,* the fear of empty spaces, any more. Indeed we should consider it bad taste to fill those empty spaces on our walls with meaningless pictures set in gorgeously carved frames, or to vary the monotony of the unbroken wall with scroll work or panels or other carved ornamentation.

Now, there is something similar in our science. We are beginning to make a point of constructing our picture of the physical universe in such a way as to represent only the facts that can be actually verified through experiment and we eschew as far as possible all voluntary theories or assumptions. We want no ornamental accessories. Just as we are no longer afraid of bare surfaces in our furniture and our dwelling rooms, so in our scientific picture of the external world we do not try to fill up the empty spaces. We try to exclude everything that in principle cannot be the object of experimental observation. And we think it better to leave our feeling of incompleteness unsatisfied rather than to introduce mental constructions which cannot by their nature be experimentally controlled or tested for their correspondence to external reality.

As an example of this I may take the development of the kinetic theory of gases. Formerly the molecules of gases were looked upon as smooth elastic balls or spheroids, like microscopic billiard balls—but *perfectly* elastic—rebounding from one another or from the walls of the container. Gradually it was found sufficient and indeed preferable to substitute for the billiard balls mechanical systems the exact nature of which can remain undefined provided only they exactly obey *mechanical* laws. These in their turn, however, came gradually to be considered as unsuitable in their application to the inner construction of the atoms and molecules, and then it turned out that the principal results given by the older gas theory could be accounted for without any other assumptions than that the laws of conservation of energy and momentum are admitted to rule the impacts of the molecules against one another or against the walls of the container. And it is even sufficient to take these laws as merely expressing averages, that is to say, holding good only for a large number of molecular impacts taken in bulk.

Another illustration is to be found in the striking attitude adopted by the modern concept of quantum mechanics as applied to the atomic problems that confronted the earlier formulation. It is a fundamental axiom of the modern quantum theory that, when giving out radiation, an atom changes from a very distinctly defined level of higher energy to a distinctly defined level of lower energy, and that it radiates a quantum of energy as a light wave whose frequency is sharply defined. Let us call the first energy level E_1, and the second E_2, then the frequency of the light wave is $\dfrac{(E_1 - E_2)}{h}$ where h is Planck's constant. It is an essential part of this theory that intermediate values of energy, between E_1, and E_2, are never encountered. Does the atom then suddenly, that is to say, timelessly, change from one energy state to another? That can't be, since the wave-train which it sends out can be proved to be of quite a considerable length, more than a yard in some cases; therefore the emission *must* require time which, from the standpoint of atomic reaction, is quite considerable. What energy has the atom during this time—that is to say, while the wave-train is being emitted? Is it E_1, or E_2? Whichever we choose to answer, certain difficulties will be involved. Because as long as the atomic energy is still E_1, the light energy would be emitted "on tick" as it were. And if the atom does the jump to E_2 before the radiation process is complete then it makes payment "in advance." In either case what happens to the sacrosanct Principle of the Conservation of Energy if, for instance, some violent interference occurred to interrupt the process, such as collision with another atom? This dilemma remained unsolved in the older quantum theory: but the newer quantum theory takes up the extraordinary attitude that the question is meaningless. We must not ask what energy the atom "really" has at any certain time, unless we can measure it. And, according to Heisenberg, that measurement is in principle impossible without an energetic interference with the system, which becomes more serious the more precise the measurement becomes (this concerns the uncertainty relation between energy and time). If we decide to carry out the measurement, then it is maintained that we shall actually find either E_1 or E_2, never an intermediate value; and also that, in exact correspondence, we shall detect in the neighborhood of the atom either the total amount of energy, E_1—E_2, in the form of radiation or nothing at all. So *if we investigate experimentally* we shall never find the Principle of Conservation of Energy violated. *If we don't,* well then—we are requested to refrain from giving any meaning at all to the conception of the *actual* energy of the system! Our world picture has to remain bare and empty in this respect—we are not afraid of the empty space on our canvas. I have been giving here the current view without criticizing it. You may call it the scientific fashion of the day, if you like, for that is what we are interested in for the purpose of the present discussion.

Desire for Change and Freedom from Authority: In nearly every branch of human activity, whether political or social or artistic or religious, there is to-day a profound skepticism in regard to traditionally accepted principles. Of course in all ages there has been a certain desire for change; otherwise life would not progress. But what strikes one most forcibly to-day is that this desire to evade being carried on the current of accepted ideas extends not only to every branch of human activity, but is also a common attitude with all classes. And furthermore the radicals as such are no longer a cranky and noisy minority; the desire for change is universal. It is a mental characteristic of our most responsible and serious people, and not merely a crazy notion of the common herd who are always ready to blame the stupidity of others for the distress they meet with in life and think that anything would be better than the present order. The tendency to belittle the worth of existing institutions shows itself most forcibly in the general attitude towards authority of every kind, especially that authority which is based on mere tradition. Everything must be submitted to independent rational scrutiny and an institution which cannot justify itself on these grounds has to go by the board. It must have something else to recommend it than mere historical development or the acceptance of former generations.

I shall not plead here in favor of this tendency nor against it. It is there and we just take it as a fact. And we find its influence very definitely felt in contemporary physics. In the case of physical science, however, we can trace the beginnings of the movement much further back than the world war. The first step in the direction of radical change was the discovery of what is called non-Euclidian geometry more than a hundred years ago. Slowly and unobtrusively but with increasing vigor the question arose as to which geometry is really true—the traditionally sacrosanct geometry of Euclid, according to which three-dimensional space is analogous to an infinitely extended plane in two dimensions, or one of the newly invented geometries presenting a definite positively or negatively *curved* space. The boldness of this idea will strike you when you remember that with positive curvature the three-dimensional space would find its two-dimensional analogue in the *surface* of a huge ball and, like the ball's surface, would be finite, though unbounded.

It is frequently reported—though I am told that it cannot be proved by anything that Gauss has written in his papers or letters—that this great mathematician, in carrying out a triangulation in North Germany, retained a certain hope of a possible experimental decision between the different geometries. For according to both types of non-Euclidian geometry the sum of the angles of a triangle should deviate from 180°, either in the positive or in the negative, the value of 180° being characteristic only for the ordinary Euclidian case, which is exactly intermediate between the two. Moreover, the deviation should be proportional to the area of the triangle. If this legend of Gauss be true, one might consider it an indication of his progressive genius, since he did not hesitate to break away from the sacred tradition, which held that anything other than the hitherto accepted geometry was *impossible*. On the other hand, if the legend is untrue, it may be because he had a still deeper insight into the question! For since that time we have learned from Henri Poincaré that an experimental decision could hardly be expected, in fact that it is in a certain sense impossible in principle. As the measurement of the angles obviously has to be carried out by means of optical instruments, it depends, in the first place, on the action of the light rays, and then on the action of the metal pivots and other accessories moving in what was perhaps non-Euclidian space. These considerations led Poincaré to the conclusion that we are absolutely free to believe any geometry we like to be true. We choose the one that is most convenient to us—that is to say, the geometry according to which the laws of nature appear in their simplest forms and according to which we can in the simplest way express the laws of transmission of light, the movement of real solid bodies, and so on.

The revolutionary tendency of contemporary physics has shown itself most strikingly in the theory of relativity and the quantum theory. The latter even throws doubt on the validity of the principle of causality. I may say here in passing that I think what applies to geometry applies also to causality. It can never be decided experimentally whether causality in nature is "true" or "untrue." The relation of cause and effect, as Hume pointed out long ago, is not something that we find in nature but is rather a characteristic of the way in which we regard nature. We are quite free to maintain this principle of causality or to alter it according to our convenience, in the sense of taking it in whatever way makes for a simpler description of natural phenomena. And it must be pointed out here that not only are we free to drop a long-accepted principle when we think we have found something more convenient from the viewpoint of physical research, but that we are also free to re-adopt the rejected principle when we find we have made a mistake in laying it aside. This mistake may easily come to light with the discovery of new facts. A developing empirical science need not and must not be afraid of being taunted with a lack of consistency between its announcements at subsequent epochs.

The Idea of Relativity and Invariance: I think that this group of ideas should be treated quite apart from its revolutionary aspect, because in itself it extends beyond the scope of physics. The idea of relativity is much older than Einstein's Theory of Relativity. The first historically known relativists of the Occident were the Greek Sophists, who held that they were able by the art of words equally to establish the truth of either the one or the other of two contradictory statements. Though such an advertisement may have been useful to solicitors and politicians, yet I am inclined to believe that the Sophists originally intended something more serious than merely to boast of their excellence in overwhelmingly persuasive talk. I am sure they meant to emphasize the truth that a statement is very seldom simply either right or wrong, but that nearly always a point of view is to be found from which it is right and another point of view from which it is wrong. Stated very generally, the kernel of the

117

relativity idea is this: Even to a very definite question precisely put (for instance: does the earth move against the medium through which light waves are propagated or does it not?), though the question apparently admits of only "Yes" or "No" as an answer, yet one sometimes has to answer by saying: That depends on how you look at it. *That depends.* But of course it is not this evasive reply which contains the great thought. The real crux is to construct this *That depends* in such a way that the contradictions which led to the dilemma cancel out.

In the example which I have alluded to the so-called aberration of the light coming from a fixed star seemed to contradict the results of the Michelson experiment. By aberration we denote the fact that the direction in which we see a fixed star alters slightly when the earth alters the direction of its movement during its yearly course. The evident inference was that the earth is moving against the light waves, just as the driver of a motor car is moving against the rain that strikes his wind shield. It looks to him as if the rain were coming against him from the front. If this inference were correct, one would further infer that in a laboratory, which is moving along with the earth, a ray of light should take a *longer* time to travel, say, from one end of the laboratory to the other end, if this happens to be the direction of motion of the earth (and therefore of the laboratory) than if it happens to be the opposite direction. For when the goal is moving towards the runner he will reach it earlier than when the goal is moving away. But the Michelson experiment proves that it takes the same time in each case. Various explanations have been put forward to meet this difficulty, but none is satisfactory. For instance, there is one which tries to explain the puzzle by suggesting that the beam of light coming from a laboratory-source takes on the velocity of the source at the moment of emission, that is to say, the earth's velocity, in much the same way as a bullet shot forward from an aeroplane receives the velocity of the fast-moving plane in addition to the velocity given it by the gun from which it is discharged.

But this hypothesis does not work. For we know of distant twin stars which revolve around one another. Now, if the above explanation were true, it would have to apply to the light emitted from the stars as well. Therefore the light which is sent out when the star is moving away from us ought to start its journey with a slower velocity than the light which is emitted some time later, when the star is moving

119

towards us. If this were so it would lead to hopeless "confusion"; for it would mean that light which had been emitted later would reach us earlier, if we suppose the change of direction of the star's motion to have taken place in the interval. But we can find no traces whatsoever of this confusion of the light coming from distant twin sources.

The extreme difficulty of reconciling all these facts ultimately gave birth to what is called the Special Theory of Relativity. Here I can only indicate its essential point. The movement of a body can be directly observed only relative to another body as a "reference system." *Now just let us try to assume* that the concept of motion has no other meaning than the relative motion of material bodies. If it were possible to formulate all laws of Nature, including the laws of optics, so that they only imply the relative velocities of material bodies, then it would follow as a matter of course that in the Michelson experiment, where all the bodies in question (the earth, the optical instruments and the observer) do not move at all in relation to one another, no velocity of a body can appear in the results of the experiment. In the case, however, of the aberration of light coming from a distant star there are in reality two material systems, namely, the observer on the earth and the fixed star. It is conceivable that their relative velocities have to be taken into account.

This case may serve also as an example of the elimination of unnecessary features in our scientific picture of the physical universe. If we eliminate the abstract notion which we call "motion" and also the notion of "simultaneity" (on which I shall not enter here), then we are face to face with those "empty spaces" which caused a certain amount of uneasiness to most of us when the idea of eliminating those features was first suggested.

The concept of Invariance is the necessary complementary idea to the general idea of relativity. If you declare that the question, which we have put, cannot be answered by "Yes" or "No"—which means to say bluntly, that we have put a nonsensical question—then let us know how we ought to formulate a question so that it will have a meaning! What things are independent of your wretched *It Depends?* In the Relativity Theory, for instance, what things are independent of the Reference System?—These questions show exactly what is meant by the concept of Invariance. Once we formulate the idea, it proves so comprehensive that all human ideation seems to be subject to it. I have said in the former chapter that in scientific practice we accept an experiment as a legitimate part of our group of established scientific data, only if the result of the experiment is reproducible. This means that it must be an Invariant, not merely in reference to the observer but in reference also to a great many other things. In short, it must be an Invariant in reference to everything except those conditions which we specially point out as essential when describing the experiment. And in a much more general sense the whole question discussed in this and the preceding chapter is a question of invariance. It is inquired whether the conclusions of physical science are invariants with reference to the cultural milieu in which we live or whether they must be referred to this milieu as a Reference Frame. If the latter be the case, when the cultural milieu undergoes a radical change the conclusions of science, even though they may not become false in detail, would yet acquire an essentially different meaning and interest.

Let us come to the next feature I have mentioned as a leading characteristic of our time. I shall call it mass control. In using this term I mean to indicate our highly-developed technique of marvellously reducing the outlay of time and labor in dealing with huge totals, the single elements of which demand individual handling. These totals are, for instance, groups of inhabitants (of a country, province, city or parish), electors, taxpayers, consumers, subscribers (to libraries, newspapers, insurance companies, railways, etc.); the masses of books in libraries, motor cars and so on. The means of controlling all these as totalities are registration, cartography, catalogues, official forms, ledgers, with organized bodies of officials in each branch whose activities are rationalized under general laws and special instructions. The making of laws and the administration of justice come under the same technique of mass control. In drawing up laws we endeavor to forecast all imaginable types of lawsuits and misdeameanors, so that we can draw up a general law which will make it easy for a judge to pass his verdict, because otherwise it would be impossible to deal in a fair and uniform way with each case as it comes up.

Last, but by no means least, comes the marvellous system of factory output whereby we can satisfy the enormous demand for goods in our time. If each typewriter, for instance, were to be turned out individually, each part being made singly for a definite machine, then the utility of the work to be done by the typewriter would never balance the immense amount of time and thought and energy put into the manufacture of it. But when we standardize the typewriter and all its parts so that one factory machine can turn out each part in series, then it is possible to manufacture typewriters in the bulk, so that the cost of each machine as a member of the mass will be in proportion to its utility. The greatest part of the expenditure for manufacturing can be made once and for all by the setting up of the necessary factory plant whereby the single parts are manufactured. By an output of many thousands a day the ingenious idea is so to speak multiplied by this factor, the expenditure for the single sample is proportionately diminished and we are left with what would really deserve the name of miracle, had we modern people not got so used to it that we buy for say ten or twelve pounds a little marvel, which as a single construction would not be available for a thousand pounds. It is to this system of mass control in manufacture that so many of our modern products owe their fabulous perfection. It really means the employment of hundreds of thousands of servants in order to make it easier for His Majesty the Consumer to have his requirements fulfilled.

The most perfect instance of our domination of matter by an organized system of control, and at the same time economizing labor by making only an initial expenditure for our working machinery, is to be found in mathematical analysis. The use of mathematical analysis is the dominating feature of physical science to-day. If a philosopher or scientist in ancient Greece were told how we solve a simple problem in hydrodynamics to-day: if he were told, for instance, that we can follow every small portion of a liquid and that we can take into account at any moment all the forces which act upon this portion, and which change continually because they issue from other sections of the liquid, the movement of which forms itself a part of the problem—the Greek would not believe that a finite human intelligence could ever perform such an intricate task, even if several years were devoted to it. Yet the problem might be one which we may give to-day as an ordinary exercise in a class room.

The fact is that we have learned how to dominate the whole process with one differential equation, thus:—

$$\frac{\partial^2 u}{\partial x^2} + \frac{\partial^2 u}{\partial y^2} + \frac{\partial^2 u}{\partial z^2} = 0$$

I have said: "With *one* equation." In reality the equation states what is true for every single particle and at any given time. The art lies in formulating our knowledge in such a way that the form of the statement is the same for every point in time and space. That is the way of adapting our knowledge so that it can be dealt with in the same manner with regard to time and labor as the manufacturer deals with his machinery.

Another example may be found in components of tensors and vectors. We write down a single letter of the alphabet with various subscripts, such as the following:—

$$\Gamma_{lm}^{k} \text{ or } R_{kl, mn}$$

The subscripts stand for some number, such as 1, 2, 3, or 4, and represent the numbers of a systematically arranged register.

Thus the first of the symbols given above is used in the General Relativity Theory to represent one of forty magnitudes which are entered in such a register. The second symbol stands for twenty various magnitudes. Such magnitudes are often connected up with one another by systems of 20, 40 or 100 equations, which have to be combined with one another in a most elaborate way. Exact rules, however (such as those for the so-called raising and lowering of the indices), bring the half dozen magnitudes or equations that are required, automatically from the drawer, so that the computation can be made just as simply and clearly as with one or two equations. These examples might be increased *ad libitum*. Economical simplification is the essential feature of mathematical progress, whereby a constantly developing sphere of investigation is brought within the practical limits of our quantitative thought.

The employment of statistics, which plays such an important rôle in modern physics and astronomy, is one of the methods that belong to our modern system of controlling huge totalities. Here, however, it has a more particular and more profound significance, for it introduces an entirely new idea which has proved marvellously productive of results. Cartography and registration are used by all of us for the purpose of securing the correct orientation quickly in regard to each single case as it turns up; but the essential feature of statistics is *the prudent and systematic ignoring of details*. This is a typical instance wherein a new trend of interest entails a shifting of all questions and gives rise to entirely new ones. Even when it is possible to secure a knowledge of the particular details regarding individual features or events, this knowledge is not what interests the statistician; for he looks out for laws of quite another kind that furnish new information. This is more easily recognized in the case of astronomy than in the case of physics. In physics it may seem to those who are not sufficiently acquainted with the essential idea that the employment of statistics indicates an acknowledgment of defeat, inasmuch as it suggests that we have fallen back on this method because we have found that it would be impossible to give a detailed account of the position and movement of single molecules, even if we wished to do so. In the case of astronomical statistics we possess the detailed knowledge but we find that it leads us nowhere. We are completely uninterested in the question whether one particular star be redder or paler, what is the intensity of the light emitted from it, whether it is moving towards us or away from us and what is the velocity of its movement. We are forced to ignore details here in order to reach conclusions which are inaccessible to any system of investigation based on the knowledge of these details. Let us quote here only one well-known case as a typical example of what I mean:—

Only in the case of comparatively few stars in the "immediate neighborhood" of the sun can we measure their distance from us directly, by the so-called parallactic displacement which takes place in the course of the year. As to the distance of the stars that are farther away we do not know anything directly; but we conclude that, *on an average,* the weaker their light appears to us the farther away they are from us. On this assumption we surmise that the weaker stars must be much more numerous than the brighter ones. And this turns out to be actually the case. It also turns out that the number of stars with decreasing brilliancy increases exactly in the same degree as might be expected if the stars, taking a broad average, were distributed uniformly throughout space and with the same density as in our immediate neighborhood. For if this be the case, then—since the brilliancy decreases in proportion to the square of the distance—we can calculate exactly the increasing number of the stars as their brilliancy decreases, and, as I said, observation shows these calculations to be correct. But only up to a certain magnitude. Beyond this we find that the number of weaker stars that can be observed ceases to increase in the way we should anticipate on the hypothesis of uniform distribution throughout space. The actual number falls more and more short of the calculated one. For stars of this definite magnitude the observer with his telescope has evidently reached the border of our "near" stellar environment—the Milky Way or Galaxy. As we know the statistical relation between magnitude and distance, we can in this way estimate the dimensions of the Milky Way in all directions (you know that it turns out to be lens-shaped), although the dimensions are far too great to allow us to ascertain the distance of a single star. In this way the judicious elimination of detail, which the statistical system has taught us, has brought about a complete transformation of our knowledge of the heavens.

It is manifest on all sides that this statistical method is a dominant feature of our epoch and an important instrument of progress in almost every sphere of public life. But it is unfortunately an instrument that is employed all too indiscriminately and without sufficient critical judgment. It appears very simple but it is extremely complex. In its application to human life, where more complex and quite unexpected features arise, it is far more difficult to handle than when dealing with stars and molecules. To add up columns and make up averages or percentages seems very simple. And thus the method itself is brought into discredit by the lack of mathematical and logical training of those who use it—not to speak of a lack of impartiality. It is so much easier to make a wrong "statistic" than a true one, that whoever has a liking for it can easily enjoy it!

The statistics of economists, sociologists, and so on—in short, human statistics—are more akin to the statistics of physics than to those of astronomy. The astronomer observes his object and cannot influence it because he is outside of it and distant from it; but the physicist and the human statistician endeavor to forecast the laws according to which the statistics will alter if the external conditions are arbitrarily changed. In a former chapter I have spoken very definitely of the "law of averages" as known in physical science. This law enables the physicist to master matter very completely, though he can never know the fate of a single molecule; nor can he affect its course.

May I be allowed to express a hope that the analogy between this state of affairs in physical science and the marked trend of our epoch will become closer as time goes on; for the ultimate goal which I have in mind at the moment is certainly not yet reached.

To establish the necessary order and lawfulness in the human community, with the least possible interference in the private affairs of the individual, seems to me to be the aim of a highly developing culture. For this purpose the statistical method as used by the physicist appears very appropriate. In the case of the human community it would mean the study of the average mind and the average human gifts, taking into account their range of variation, and from this to infer what the motives are that must be put before human beings to appeal to their desires so as to secure a social order that is at least *bearable* in all its essential features.

VI

WHAT IS A LAW OF NATURE?[1]

THE laws of physics are generally looked upon as a paradigm of exactitude. Therefore one would naturally take it for granted that probably no other science would be able to give such a clear and definite answer when asked what is meant when we speak of a law of nature.

---

[1] (Inaugural Address at the University of Zurich, December 9th, 1922.) This address was not printed on the occasion of its delivery. Some time afterwards the development of quantum mechanics brought Exner's ideas into the foreground of scientific interest, without, however, Exner's name being mentioned. The text as here printed follows the original manuscript from which the address was read.

What is a Law of Nature? The answer does not really seem to be very difficult. When man's higher consciousness first awakens he finds himself in an environment whose changing elements are of the highest significance for his weal or woe. Experience —first the unsystematized experience of his daily struggle for life and afterwards the experience derived from systematically and rationally planned scientific experiments—shows him that the natural processes which take place in his environment do not follow one another in an arbitrary, kaleidoscopic manner, but that they present a notable degree of regularity. He eagerly strives to become acquainted with the nature of this regularity, because such knowledge will be of tremendous advantage to him in his struggle for life. The order of nature thus perceived by man is of the same type throughout. Certain features in the succession of natural events always and everywhere show themselves to be connected with certain other features. Of special biological significance is that case in which the one group of characters *precedes* the other group in time. The circumstances preceding a certain happening (A) which is often observed in nature, divide themselves into two typical groups: (1) circumstances that are *always* present—the invariable, and (2) those which are only sometimes present—the variable. When it is further discovered that conversely the unchanging group is *always* followed by A, this discovery gives rise to the statement that this invariable group of circumstances is the *cause* that brings about the phenomenon A. Thus, hand-in-hand with the discovery of *special* regular connections, we come to the idea of a *general necessary* connectedness between one phenomenon and others as an abstraction from the mass of connections as a whole. Above and beyond our actual experience, the general postulate is laid down that in those cases in which we have not yet succeeded in isolating the causal source of any specific phenomenon, such a source must surely exist —in other words, that every natural process or event is absolutely and quantitatively determined at least through the totality of the circumstances or physical conditions that accompany its appearance. This postulate is sometimes called the "principle of causality." Our belief in it has been steadily confirmed again and again by the progressive discovery of causes that specially condition each event.

Now, what we call a "law of nature" is nothing else than any one of the regularities observed in natural occurrences, insofar as it is looked upon as necessary, in the sense of the above-mentioned postulate.

Is there still some obscurity here, some occasion for doubt? And, if so, where? Since about the actual facts there can be no doubt whatever, the only questionable feature is the justifiability or universal applicability of the causal postulate.

Within the past four or five decades physical research has clearly and definitely shown—strange discovery—that *chance* is the common root of all the rigid conformity to Law that has been observed, at least in the overwhelming majority of natural processes, the regularity and invariability of which have led to the establishment of the postulate of universal causality.

In order to produce a physical process wherein we observe such conformity to Law innumerable thousands, often billions, of single atoms or molecules must combine. (For professional physicists I may say here in parenthesis that this is also true of those phenomena in which, as we often say to-day, the effect produced by a single atom can be successfully studied; because in truth the interaction of this atom with thousands of others determines the observed effect.) In a very large number of cases of totally different types, we have now succeeded in explaining the observed regularity as completely due to the tremendously large number of molecular processes that are coöperating. The individual process may, or may not, have its own strict regularity. In the observed regularity of the mass phenomenon the individual regularity (if any) need not be considered as a factor. On the contrary, it is completely effaced by averaging millions of single processes, the average values being the only things that are observable to us. The average values manifest their own purely *statistical regularity*, which they would also do if the outcome of each single molecular process were determined by the throwing of dice, the spinning of a roulette wheel or the drawing of sweepstake tickets from a drum.

The statistical interpretation of the laws is illustrated in the simplest and clearest manner by the phenomena of gases, from which, by the way, the new ideas started. In this case the individual process is the collision of two gas molecules, either with one another or with the wall of the container. The pressure of the gas against the walls of the container was formerly attributed to a specific expansive force of

137

matter in the gaseous state; but according to the molecular theory it is due to the bombardment of the molecules. The number of collisions per second against one square centimeter of the surface of the wall is tremendous. For atmospheric pressure at zero degrees Centigrade it runs into twenty-four figures $(2.2. \times 10^{23})$. Even in the most complete terrestrial vacuum and for only one square millimeter and only one-thousandth of a second the number still runs into a figure of eleven places. Besides giving a complete account of the so-called gas laws, that is, of the dependence of pressure on temperature and volume, the molecular theory also explains all other properties of real gases, such as friction, heat conduction, diffusion—and this *purely statistically,* as a consequence of the molecules being exchanged between different parts of the gas by individual processes of the utmost irregularity. In performing the corresponding calculations and discussing the relevant considerations we generally assume the validity of the mechanical laws for the single happening, the collision. But it must be stated that this is not at all ncessary. It would be quite sufficient to assume that at each individual collision an increase in mechanical energy and mechanical momentum is just as probable as a decrease, so that taking the *average* of a great many collisions, these quantities remain constant in much the same way as two dice cubes, if thrown a million times, will yield the average 7 whereas the result of each single throw is a pure matter of chance.

From what has been said it follows that the statistical interpretation of the gas laws is *possible,* perhaps also that it is the most simple; yet we cannot conclude that it is the *only possible* interpretation. But a crucial test is furnished by the following experiment. If the pressure of a gas is really only a statistical average value it must be subject to *fluctuations*. These must become all the more obvious the more the number of coöperating elementary processes is reduced by reducing (1) the surface against which the pressure is exerted and (2) the inertia of the body which experiences the pressure, in order to allow a prompt reaction to a fluctuation that occurs within a short period of time. Both these conditions can be attained by suspending tiny, ultra-microscopical particles in the gas. These actually show a zig-zag movement of extreme irregularity, long known as the Brownian movement, which never comes to rest and agrees in all particulars with the theoretical predictions. Although the number of molecules which hit the particle during a measurable period of time is still very large, it is yet not large enough to produce an absolutely uniform pressure from all sides. Through a chance preponderance of the impact in a chance direction, which changes quite irregularly from moment to moment, the particle will be driven hither and thither on quite an irregular path. Here, therefore, we see a law of nature—the law of gas pressure—losing its exact validity in proportion as the *number* of coöperating individual processes decreases. One cannot easily imagine a more convincing proof of the essentially statistical character of at least *this* law.

I could here mention numerous other cases that have been experimentally and theoretically investigated, such as the uniform blue of the sky, which results from entirely irregular variations of atmospheric densities (consequent upon their molecular constitution), or the strictly law-governed decay of radioactive substances which results from the disintegration of the individual atoms, whereby it appears to depend entirely on chance whether an individual atom will disintegrate immediately or to-morrow or in a year's time. But however many examples are considered, they scarcely suffice to render our belief

140

in the statistical character of physical laws as certain as does the fact that the Second Law of Thermodynamics, or Law of Entropy, *which plays a rôle in positively every physical process,* has clearly proved to be the *prototype* of statistical law. Although this matter would justify a closer examination, on account of its extraordinary interest, I must confine myself here to the very cursory remark that empirically the Law of Entropy is very intimately connected with the typical one-directional character of all natural processes. Although the Law of Entropy by itself is not sufficient to determine the direction in which the state of a material system will change in the next instant, it always *excludes certain directions of change,* the direction exactly opposite to the one which actually occurs being *always* excluded. By virtue of the statistical method the Law of Entropy has taken on the following content: namely, that every process or event proceeds from a relatively improbable—that is to say, more or less molecularly ordered—state to a more probable one—that is to say, to a state of increasing disorder among the molecules.

In regard to what I have said up to now there is no essential difference of opinion among physicists. But the case is otherwise in regard to what I shall have to say from now on.

Although we have discovered physical laws to be of a statistical character, which does not necessarily imply the strictly causal determination of individual molecular processes, still the general opinion is that we should find the individual process—for instance, the collision of two gas molecules—determined by rigid causality, if we could trace it. (In a similar way the result of a game of roulette would not be something haphazard for any one who could measure exactly the impetus given to the wheel, the resistance of the air, the friction on the axis, etc., etc.) In some cases, among which is also the one of colliding gas molecules, it is even claimed that quite definite features of the individual process can be ascertained; viz., the conservation of energy and momentum at every single impact, not merely in the average.

It was the experimental physicist, Franz Exner, who for the first time, in 1919, launched a very acute philosophical criticism against the *taken-for-granted* manner in which the absolute determinism of molecular processes was accepted by everybody. He came to the conclusion that the assertion of determinism was certainly *possible*, yet by no means *necessary*, and when more closely examined *not at all very probable.*

As to the non-necessity, I have already given my opinion; and I believe with Exner that it can be upheld, even despite the fact that most physicists claim quite definite characteristics for the elementary laws which they postulate. Naturally we *can* explain the energy principle on the large scale by its already holding good in the single events. But I do not see that we are *bound* to do so. In like manner we *can* explain the expansive force of a gas as the sum of the expansive forces of its elementary particles. But this interpretation is *here* decidedly incorrect, and I do not see why *there* it should be looked upon as the *only possible* one. I may further remark that the energy-momentum theorem provides us with only *four* equations, thus leaving the elementary process to a great extent undetermined, even if it complies with them.

Whence arises the widespread belief that the behavior of molecules is determined by absolute causality, whence the conviction that the contrary is *unthinkable?* Simply from the *custom,* inherited through thousands of years, of *thinking causally,* which makes the idea of determined events, of absolute, primary causalness, seem complete nonsense, a *logical* absurdity.

But from what source was this habit of causal thinking derived? Why, from observing for hundreds and thousands of years precisely *those regularities* in the natural course of events which, in the light of our present knowledge, are most certainly *not governed by causality;* or at least not so governed essentially, since we now know them to be *statistically* regulated phenomena. Therewith this traditional habit of thinking loses its rational foundation. In practice, of course, the habit may safely be retained, since it predicts the outcomes satisfactorily. But to allow this habit to force upon us the postulate that, behind the observed statistical regularities, there must be causal laws, would quite obviously involve a logically vicious circle.

Not only are there no considerations that *force* this assumption upon us, but we should realize, still further, that such a duality in the laws of Nature is somewhat improbable. On the one hand we should have the intrinsic, genuine, absolute laws of the infinitesimal domain; while on the other there would be that observed macroscopic regularity of events which in its most essential features is *not* due to the existence of the genuine laws but is determined rather by the concept of *pure number*, the most translucent and simple creation of the human mind. Clear and definite intelligibility in the world of outer appearances, and behind this a dark, eternally unintelligible imperative, a mysterious Kismet! The *possibility* that this may be in reality the case must be admitted; but this duplication of natural law so closely resembles the animistic duplication of natural *objects*, that I cannot regard it as at all tenable.

It must not be supposed, however, that I consider it a simple and easy matter to carry through and defend this new, a-causal (i.e., *not necessarily* causal) point of view. The ruling opinion to-day is that at least the laws of gravitation and electro-dynamics are of the absolute, elementary type, that they also govern the world of atoms and electrons and are perhaps at the basis of everything as *the* primary and fundamental Law. You are all familiar with the amazing success of Einstein's gravitation theory. Must we conclude from this that his gravitational equations are an *elementary law?* I hardly think so. In no case of a natural process is the number of single atoms which must coöperate in order that an observable effect may be produced so vast as in the case of gravitational phenomena. This would explain, from the statistical

145

point of view, why we can attain such extraordinary accuracy in forecasting movements of the planets centuries ahead. Moreover I shall not deny that Einstein's theory yields powerful support to the belief in the *absolute validity of the energy and momentum principles.* With reference to the particle, these principles actually involve nothing more than a tendency towards absolute perseverance. For Einstein's gravitation theory is not really anything more than the reduction of gravitation to the law of inertia. That under certain conditions *nothing changes* is surely the simplest Law that can be conceived, and hardly falls within the concept of causal determination. It may after all be reconcilable with a strictly a-causal view of Nature.

In contradistinction to gravitation, the laws of electro-dynamics are quite generally applied to-day to processes within the atom itself, and indeed with amazing success. These positive results will be considered the most serious objection that can be advanced against the a-causal view. The space at my disposal does not allow of my going further into this question. I must confine myself to the following general remark, which at the same time briefly sums up the conclusions we have reached:—

Exner's assertion amounts to this: It is quite possible that Nature's laws are of thoroughly statistical character. The demand for an absolute law in the background of the statistical law—a demand which at the present day almost everybody considers imperative—*goes beyond the reach of experience.* Such a dual foundation for the orderly course of events in Nature is in itself improbable. *The burden of proof falls on those who champion absolute causality, and not on those who question it.* For a doubtful attitude in this respect is to-day by far the *more natural.*

The electro-dynamic theory of the atom appears unsuited to furnish the proof, because this theory itself is universally recognized to be suffering from serious intrinsic incoherences which are often felt to be of a logical character. I prefer to believe that, once we have discarded our rooted predilection for absolute Causality, we shall succeed in overcoming these difficulties, rather than expect atomic theory to substantiate the dogma of Causality.

147

VII

CONCEPTUAL MODELS IN PHYSICS AND THEIR PHILOSOPHICAL VALUE[1]

I BELIEVE that every one interested in the progress of research into the structure of matter, during the past few decades, must occasionally have felt like a suddenly awakened somnambulist, taken by surprise in face of the amazingly precise and detailed assertions which we claim to be able to prove. At such moments we are inclined to exclaim: Heavens! Is all that really proved and certain? Do these atoms and electrons, etc., really exist and, if so,

---

[1] Address delivered before the Physical Society of Frankfort-on-Main, December 8th, 1928.

are they in precisely the configurations we attribute to them? Is their existence, as many declare, as definitely guaranteed as the objects of my environment which can be touched and handled?

Let us take any object near at hand—this little fruit basket, for instance—and ask why, and in what sense, we attribute real existence to it. In what way does it differ from a picture of a fruit basket or from an hallucination? More exact analysis shows that this fruit basket is really nothing more than a *frame* which serves to unite certain sense-perceptions, some of which are actual, whereas the majority are only virtual; and we anticipate their occasional occurrence in definite relationship to one another. The visual image will endure as long as we do not change our standpoint, and thus it differs from an hallucination. It will change in quite a definite way when we change our standpoint in regard to it. We expect certain tactile sensations if we touch it, sensations of taste if we bite through a fruit, a crackling of the basket if we press it together. We are usually not aware of all these expectations; we focus them unconsciously into what we call a fruit basket which really exists. And so it is with other objects in our environment. That is the *reality* which surrounds us: some actual perceptions

149

and sensations become automatically supplemented by a number of virtual perceptions and appear connected in independent complexes, which we call existing *objects*. Different human individuals accomplish this supplementation in very different degrees, and more or less vividly. We characterize them as alert or slow-witted, stupid or clever, intelligent or ignorant.

I believe that, with respect to objects of science, we cannot really attribute another meaning than the one just indicated to the concept of "really existing." For the sciences of biology, geology and astronomy it is easy to show that this is the case. The biology of living species does not depart notably from the modes of thought of every-day life. Paleobiology and geology, when they speak of what took place on the earth thousands or millions of years ago, supplement what has been actually experienced by the virtual, and in principle possible, observations of a human witness retrojected into that time of long ago. The matter is perhaps a little more subtle in the case of astronomy. But still its statements have, correctly speaking, no other meaning except in connection with virtual observations. We are all familiar with the habit of popular lecturers in saying to their audiences, e.g., that if one could sit in an aeroplane going at a rate of two hundred miles an hour one would, in order to arrive at such and such a star, require so much time, etc.

Now let us turn to the objects of *Physics*. What perplexes us here, from the epistemological point of view, is the preoccupation as to whether in this case, in principle, virtual observations are at all conceivable, on which the "real existence" of these objects can be based. This preoccupation is not unjustified. It arises from the extraordinary subtlety of the supposed structures. Consider the space-lattice of a crystal, or Bohr's atom, with its nucleus and interlacing electron orbits. Large-scale models of these can be observed on all sides, and handled. Is there anything, any kind of observation, which could be performed or at least imagined to be performed with the atoms and electrons themselves, and which would correspond to the visibility and tangibility of a large-scale model?

You know where the difficulties lie, with respect to visibility. You know that these structures are much too fine to form an image by means of light that is visible to our eyes. There is a limit to the efficiency of the microscope; for only structures whose minuteness is not less than about the wave-length of light can be perceived to some extent. As to the objects in

question, ordinary light is many thousand times too
coarse to reveal their structure. We should have to
employ finer light—the short wave X-rays. And with
these there is actually one case—the space-lattice of
a crystal—in which we have been so successful that
we are justified in answering the question as to its
virtual visibility in the affirmative. The Laue diffraction figure of a crystal with X-rays is entirely analogous to the diffraction figure produced by a micro-
scopical object in the focal plane. It is true that we
have no lenses which would actually focus this to
an image; but we can so unmistakably infer what
the nature of the image would be that we can thus,
in an entirely satisfactory way, dispense with the
actual observation.

Now, how is it in the case of the atom? To a certain extent the Laue diagrams give us an equally direct insight into the arrangement of electrons within
the atom. The atoms are situated in the lattice points,
and one can infer from the diagram that what scatters
(electrons, according to the theory) has a definite
spatial extension and arrangement: but unfortunately,
after we have obtained this very refined *spatial* analysis, the want of precision in our means of analyzing
the events with respect to *time* stands in the way of

152

further progress. We cannot get direct evidence of the instantaneous distribution of the "scattering substance," but only of the average distribution for a period of time, during which the electrons in Bohr's model are supposed to have executed very many revolutions, sweeping the whole spatial region in the neighborhood of the nucleus (for the orbits are not exactly periodic, but execute precessions and revolutions of the perihelia). Thus we are not concerned here with actually locating the individual electrons at certain points, nor even with discriminating the shape of their orbits. If the "scattering substance" were continuously spatially distributed in a diffuse manner it would produce the same impression.

Of course the virtual observation, on which to base our conviction that electron orbits really exist, need not be a visual one, similar to an act of sight. We might argue that the electrons, being field centers, naturally cannot be directly "seen." All that is observable in their case is their field. From macroscopic experiments we know the laws that govern the field of moving electric charges and we further know the laws according to which the electrons move in an external electro-magnetic field, principally from experiments with cathode rays. To assert that *really such* electrons, as we are acquainted with in cathode rays, move in these tiny orbits *can* have no other meaning than that they move according to the same laws and are surrounded by a field, as in a cathode ray. For in this case, too, the electron is to our mind nothing but a field center influenced by the external field in a special way. Let us ask then: Can it be maintained that in principle it is possible, by exact registration of the electro-magnetic alternating field, which surrounds a single atom, to infer the revolutions of the electrons as described in Bohr's theory?

You know that the answer is in the negative. And indeed quite independently of the question whether or not one considers it possible to obtain such an exact field registration of the individual atom. Not only do the orbits themselves not obey "the ordinary laws of electro-dynamics," but the *field* is also totally different from what might be expected. It is made up of quite other frequencies than the frequencies of electron revolutions are supposed to be. The average effect resulting from the coöperation of many atoms suffices to reveal this discrepancy, which was admitted in Bohr's theory from the very start.

Once we have become aware of this state of affairs, the epistemological question: "Do the electrons really exist in these orbits within the atom?" is to be answered with a decisive *No*, unless we prefer to say that the putting of the question itself has absolutely no meaning. Indeed there does not seem to be much sense in inquiring about the real existence of something, if one is convinced that the effect through which the thing would manifest itself, in case it existed, is certainly *not* observed. Despite the *immeasurable* progress which we owe to Bohr's theory, I consider it very regrettable that the long and successful handling of its models has blunted our theoretical delicacy of feeling with reference to such questions. We must not hesitate to sharpen it again, lest we may be in too great haste to content ourselves with the new theories which are now supplanting Bohr's theory, and believe that we have reached the goal which indeed is still far away.

I do not intend to expound here these new theories, not even in their fundamental characteristics. What I wish to deal with is a new point of view which has manifested itself in their development, and which has remarkable consequences as regards philosophy. Recall to mind the efficiency limit of the microscope, of which I spoke before. Consider a texture whose meshes or interstices are, let us say, 100 Å in width.[1] With visible light of wave length $\lambda =$ a few 1000 Å, this structure cannot be made visible, simply because so fine a structure cannot be impressed on so coarse-grained an agent. But if we employ X-rays of $\lambda = 1$ Å we shall succeed without difficulty. This limit of observation is a relative one, depending on the fineness of the light employed. Now the new discovery (or presumed discovery) of which I wish to speak maintains that there is an *absolute* limit of a similar kind, *Nature itself, not containing more than a definite amount of structural detail, at least insofar as she is accessible to any observation at all* and what is over and above this is not the object of scientific research. Certain details are supposed to be missing in Nature as a whole in much the same way that yellow light diffracted by too fine a tissue simply will not contain its structural details (this being the reason why they cannot be detected in the diffraction image).

This absolute limit, however, is not a purely spatial one—in this the analogy fails. With respect to space

[1] (Translator's note.) Å is the initial of a Swedish physicist's name (Ångström) and is used for a unit length equal to the ten-millionth part of a millimeter. One inch equals 254 million Å units.

we can, in principle, increase precision arbitrarily—we need only employ light of shorter and shorter wave lengths. The limit is concerned with space and time simultaneously, which is fairly satisfactory, since it is precisely that *union of space and time* on the basis of which, according to relativity theory, we are to construct our physical world outlook.

To make this a little clearer let us return to the practical example to which I referred previously. By employing short-wave X-rays we have succeeded in refining discrimination in space to within atomic dimensions; but the lack of time for discrimination prevented us after all from attaining more than a blurred scheme (blurred with respect to time) of the electronic arrangement.[1]

Another example of a purely theoretical kind is the following. We measure atomic energy by measuring frequency[2] according to the fundamental equation of the Quantum Theory:

$$E = h\nu$$

To measure frequency we need a certain *time*. Let us

---

[1] Footnote. (In what follows small print indicates those sections which may be omitted by readers not interested in the somewhat technical issues.)

[2] (Translator's note.) The term "frequency" has here the same meaning as in wireless transmission, only the frequencies involved are usually much higher in the atom.

think of the primitive procedure of actually counting n vibrations within a definite time Δt. Then:

$$\nu = \frac{n}{\Delta t}$$

but manifestly with a possible error of $\Delta \nu = \dfrac{1}{\Delta t}$ because the process of counting necessarily results in giving a whole number, which is subject to an error of $\pm \frac{1}{2}$. This entails a possible error with respect to energy of $\Delta E = \dfrac{h}{\Delta t}$; hence $\Delta t \times \Delta E = h$.

The product of the uncertainty with respect to energy multiplied by the uncertainty with respect to time, has the order of magnitude of Planck's constant h. Now, relativistically, the energy is the fourth component of the energy-momentum vector; the time, that of the vector of position. Therefore the uncertainty relation can be transferred to the other components as well, for example:

$$\Delta x \cdot \Delta p_x = h,$$

where p_x is the momentum in the x-direction. Thus two variables are always associated together, each of which affects the accuracy of the other, the product of their uncertainties being h (in order of magnitude). They are what in Hamiltonian mechanics are called "conjugate" variables.

These ideas, which originated with Heisenberg, are satisfactory in a way, since they console us for the unsuccessful attempts we had made to claim the predicate of real existence for our detailed schemata by means of virtual (if not actual) observations. Evidently we have, in some cases, believed in the feasibility of observations which are impracticable, and that is why we were involved in contradictions—contradictions of the type that light shares the properties of an undulatory radiation *and* of a corpuscular radiation (the same difficulty appearing for the cathode rays, as we know to-day). On the other hand, however, Heisenberg's idea is profoundly disconcerting. It makes it exceedingly difficult to use all the terms and concepts we have employed hitherto. Many serious questions that were previously asked are rendered illusory. To inquire what is the energy of a system at a definite *instant* is now supposed to have no meaning. But then the problem which ardently interested us before, namely, whether energy actually passed by jumps or in a steady flow from one atom to another, naturally becomes illusory. The position and velocity of a particle cannot both be accurately indicated simultaneously. Thus, since the particle now becomes a thing which does *not* describe a definite path, the question as to which path it describes is illusory, in the way it was expressed hitherto. The new line of thought clearly prohibits the construction of any schemes or models extending throughout space and time and filling it, so to speak, continuously and unambiguously without leaving gaps in our supposed knowledge. Maybe the world that can be observed (and no other world matters to us as physicists) is no *continuum* at all. Of course, when faced with the question of how to represent it *otherwise*, we are still confronted by an insoluble conundrum. I do believe that we cannot be satisfied in the long run with the answer which I once received in conversation with a young physicist of outstanding genius [1]: Beware of forming models or pictures at all!

It is very remarkable that the new point of view, of which we are speaking, was first recognized while employing a very definite model of nature, which determines the events at every point of space and instant of time more completely and unambiguously than any of the former models. I allude to the so-called wave-mechanics. That seems indeed astonishing. But if Heisenberg be right, if this fundamental restriction of our observational accuracy really exists, it is not very surprising that we who are familiar with the analogous situation in wave optics should find an

[1] Professor P. A. M. Dirac.

undulatory theory of matter specially suitable, in order to understand this *universal* limit.

We need but replace the particle by a wave-group and let the wave-length λ and the momentum P have the relation:

$$P = \frac{h}{\lambda}$$

In order to build up such a group a certain λ— interval is required. Let Δx be the length of the group, then it can be shown that the ratio $\frac{\Delta x}{\lambda}$ must be allowed to vary by one unit (this ratio indicating the number of wave-crests along the group). Thus:

$$\Delta x \quad \cdot \quad \Delta \left(\frac{1}{\lambda}\right) = 1$$

Multiply by h, then $h \, \Delta \frac{1}{\lambda}$ is the uncertainty Δp. And so
$$\Delta x \cdot \quad \Delta p = h.$$

The *mathematical* relation between the uncertainty principle and the wave theory is extremely simple. The difficulty is what philosophical attitude to adopt towards this relation. One may believe either (1) that matter has *really* a wave structure. Then the uncertainty principle is an immediate consequence. Or (2) one may think that the uncertainty principle is the more fundamental. The wave theory then is

161

simply an auxiliary construction for the convenience of grasping and representing the principle.

The relation of the uncertainty principle to the older presentations of the quantum theory is very peculiar. Here it must first be called to mind that, properly speaking, the principle was known long ago. Think of Planck's work on quantum statistics, of his dividing the phase space into cells and maintaining that there is no meaning in carrying statistics further than to indicate in which of the cells of magnitude h or h^3 or h^f for 3 or f degrees of freedom respectively) the point, representing the system, is situated. That corresponds exactly to adopting Heisenberg's uncertainty h for every pair of canonical conjugate variables. In its further development we were more inclined to the following interpretation: "In reality" the phase point is situated on the boundaries of the cells, which corresponds to a sharp quantization. Now when we remember that Heisenberg's uncertainty relation corresponds exactly to the cell dimensions—that it just fills them out, so to speak—then we become extremely alarmed, since this is equivalent to abolishing sharp quantization completely, because the uncertainty corresponds exactly to the distance between adjacent energy levels.

Now it is not quite so, although at first sight it appears so. Let us apply the uncertainty relation to one of the so-called "action variables" J and its canonically conjugate "angle variable" w:

$$\Delta w \quad \cdot \quad \Delta J = h.$$

What we call sharp quantization consists precisely in restricting all the J's (the action variables) to integral multiples of h. On the other hand the w's are quantities with respect to which everything is periodic with period 1; that is to say, $w + 1$ means the same as w (just as an angle of 369° means the same as an angle of 9°). Therefore the *greatest* possible "inaccuracy" Δw actually seems to be unity, with a corresponding *smallest* value of $\Delta J = h$, that is to say equal to the whole quantum step. In order to be able to speak of anything like *sharp* quantization, ΔJ must of course be made *much* smaller, which cannot be done, *unless after all we admit much larger values of Δw.* The physical meaning of having to admit an uncertainty of the angle variable much greater than the period is obviously that sharp quantization is not a property which the system can be said to possess at a definite moment. It is a property which cannot even be ascertained after *one* revolution, but only after the system has undergone a great many revolutions.

Let us return to our original consideration. We doubted whether the detailed images, by which we try to visualize the structure of matter, might be thought of as "really existing" in the same sense as palpable objects around us, the fruit basket for instance. Do they resemble the latter in being the scaffolding for a series of *perceptions,* which can be conceived, if not actually experienced?

We were allowed to answer this question in the affirmative in many cases, such as the space-lattice of the atoms in a crystal. Yet our doubts seem to be confirmed in the most brutal fashion by the attitude which quantum theory forces upon us (as discussed in the last sections). If the claim to "real existence" be based on the possibility of at least conceiving (if not performing) certain observations, and if the observations in question be *in principle* restricted by an impassable limit, then our claim for "real existence" will be in vain, not only with respect to the particular models of the interior of the atom, to which we had clung up to the present, (following Rutherford and Bohr) but also with respect to any other model which is satisfactorily distinct and definite.

To this desperate situation let me add a word of consolation from the philosophical point of view. We must remember, after all, that it really is the ultimate purpose of all schemes and models to serve as scaffolding for any observations that are at all conceivable. The prohibition against clothing them with details, that are by no possible means observable, is a matter for no more regret than was formerly caused by our ignorance as to whether the "microscopic tennis ball" electron was red, yellow or white. If Heisenberg's assertion be correct, and if it appears at first sight to make gaps in our picture of the world which cannot be filled, then the obvious thing to do is to eliminate the regions which refuse to be filled with thought; in other words, to form a view of the world which does not contain those regions at all. Of course that is not quite easy; because the regions in question are not certain domains in space and time (not, to put it bluntly, the interiors of the atoms!) but domains of abstract thought. Yet I definitely believe that the elimination ought to be possible without leading to the consequence, that no visualizable scheme of the physical universe whatever will prove feasible. The situation will turn out similarly to that of the "color of the electron." [1] The clearness of the idea of the electron was not seriously interfered with by the fact that the property of possessing this or that definite color, though common to all perceptible objects, could not be attributed to the electron. In the same way it will be necessary to acquire a definite sense of what is *irrelevant* in our new models and schemes, before we can trust to their guidance with more equanimity and confidence.

---

[1] (Note added in translation.) It need hardly be emphasized that this example is a fictitious one, which never actually worried the mind of a physicist!

VIII

THE FUNDAMENTAL IDEA
OF WAVE MECHANICS[1]

WHEN a ray of light passes through an optical
instrument, such as a telescope or a photographic lens, it undergoes a change of direction as it
strikes each refractive or reflective surface. We can
describe the path of the light ray once we know the
two simple laws which govern the change of direction.
One of these is the law of refraction, which was discovered by Snell about three hundred years ago; and
the other is the law of reflection, which was known to

---

[1] Nobel Address delivered at Stockholm on December 12th, 1933.

Archimedes nearly two thousand years before. Figure 1 gives a simple example of a ray, A—B, passing through two lenses and undergoing a change of direction at each of the four surfaces in accordance with Snell's law.

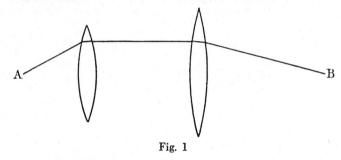

Fig. 1

From a much more general point of view, Fermat summed up the whole career of a light ray. In passing through media of varying optical densities light is propagated at correspondingly varying speeds, and the path which it follows is such as would have to be chosen by the light if it had the purpose of arriving *within the shortest possible time* at the destination which it actually reaches. (Here it may be remarked, in parenthesis, that any two points along the path of the light ray can be chosen as the points of departure and arrival respectively.) Any deviation from the path which the ray has actually chosen would mean a

167

delay. This is Fermat's famous *Principle of Least Time*. In one admirably concise statement it defines the whole career of a ray of light, including also the more general case where the nature of the medium does not change suddenly but alters gradually from

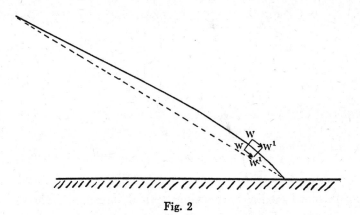

Fig. 2

point to point. The atmosphere surrounding our earth is an example of this. When a ray of light, coming from outside, enters the earth's atmosphere, the ray travels more slowly as it penetrates into deeper and increasingly denser layers. And although the difference in the speed of propagation is extremely small, yet under these circumstances Fermat's Principle demands that the ray of light must bend earthwards (see

168

Fig. 2), because by doing so it travels for a somewhat longer time in the higher "speedier" layers and comes sooner to its destination than if it were to choose the straight and shorter way (the dotted line in Fig. 2, the small quadrangle WW W¹W¹ to be ignored for the present). Most people will have noticed how the sun no longer presents the shape of a circular disk when it is low on the horizon, but is somewhat flattened, its vertical diameter appearing shortened. That phenomenon is caused by the bending of the light rays as they traverse the earth's atmosphere.

According to the wave theory of light, what we call light rays have, correctly speaking, only a fictitious meaning. They are not the physical tracks of any particles of light, but a purely mathematical construction. The mathematician calls them "orthogonal trajectories" of the wave-fronts, that is, lines which at every point run at right angles to the wave-surface. Hence they point in the direction in which the light is propagated and, as it were, guide the light's propagation. (See Fig. 3, which represents the simplest case of concentric spherical wave-fronts and the corresponding rectilinear rays, while Fig. 4 illustrates the case of bent rays.) It seems strange that a general principle of such great importance as that of Fermat should be stated directly in reference to these mathematical lines, which are only a mental construction, and not in reference to the wave-fronts themselves. One might therefore be inclined to take it merely for a mathematical curiosity. But that would be a serious mistake. For only from the viewpoint of the wave theory does this principle become directly and immediately intelligible and cease to be a miracle. What we called *bending* of the light ray presents itself to the wave theory as a *turning* of the wave-front, and is much more readily understood. For that is just what we must expect in consequence of the fact that neighboring portions of the wave-front advance at various speeds; the turning is effected in the same way as with a company of soldiers marching in line, who are ordered to "right wheel." Here the soldiers in each rank take steps of varying lengths, the man on the right wing taking the shortest steps and the man on the left taking the longest. In the case of atmospheric refraction (Fig. 2) consider a small portion WW of the wave-surface. This portion must

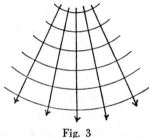

Fig. 3

170

necessarily perform a "right wheel" towards W'W,[1] because its left part is in the somewhat higher and rarer air and therefore is moving forward faster than the right, which is in the deeper layer.[1] Now in examining the case more closely it is found that the statement made in Fermat's Principle is virtually identical with the trivial and obvious assertion that, because the velocity of light varies from point to point, the wavefront must turn, as in the instance I have referred to. I cannot prove that here; but I shall try to show that it is quite reasonable.

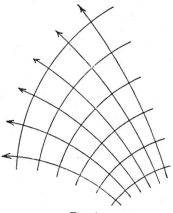

Fig. 4

Let us revert to the row of soldiers marching in line. To prevent the front rank losing its perfect alignment, let us suppose that a long pole is placed abreast of the

[1] In passing, I may call attention to a point in which Snell's concept fails. A ray of light emitted horizontally ought to remain horizontal, because in the horizontal direction the index of refraction does not vary. But, as a matter of fact, a horizontal ray is deflected to a greater degree than any other. According to the concept of the "wheeling" wave-front, this is obvious.

men and that each man holds it firmly with his hand against his chest. No word of command as to direction is given, but simply the order that each man must march or run as fast as he can. If the condition of the ground slowly changes from place to place, then either the left or the right section of the line advances more quickly than the other and this inevitably produces quite spontaneously a wheeling of the whole line to the right or left respectively. After a time it will be noticed that the line of advance, when looked upon as a whole, is not straight, but shows a definite curvature. Now this curved route is precisely the one along which the soldiers reach any place on their way *in the shortest possible time,* taking into account the nature of the ground. Although this may seem remarkable there is actually nothing strange about it, for after all, by hypothesis, each soldier has done his best to travel as quickly as possible. And it may be further noticed that the bending will always have taken place in the direction towards which the condition of the ground underfoot is less favorable; so that finally it will appear as if the marchers had purposely avoided unfavorable conditions by making a detour around those regions where they would have found their forward pace slackened.

172

Thus Fermat's Principle directly appears as the *trivial quintessence* of the wave theory. Hence it was a very remarkable event when Hamilton one day made the theoretical discovery that the orbit of a mass point moving in a field of force (for instance, of a stone thrown in the gravitational field of the earth or of some planet in its course around the sun) is governed by a very similar general principle, which thenceforth bore the name of the discoverer and made him famous. Although Hamilton's principle does not precisely consist in the statement that the mass point chooses the quickest way, yet it states something *so* similar—that is to say, it is *so closely* analogous to the principle of minimum light time—that one is faced with a puzzle. It seemed as if Nature had effected exactly the same thing twice, but in two very different ways—once, in the case of light, through a fairly transparent wave-mechanism, and on the other occasion, in the case of mass points, by methods which were utterly mysterious, unless one was prepared to believe in some underlying undulatory character in the second case also. But at first sight this idea seemed impossible. For the laws of mechanics had at that time only been established and confirmed experimentally on a large scale for bodies

173

of visible and (in the case of the planets) even huge dimensions which played the rôle of "mass points," so that something like an "undulatory nature" here appeared to be inconceivable.

The smallest and ultimate constructive elements in the constitution of matter, which we now call "mass points" in a much more particular sense, were at that time purely hypothetical. It was not until the discovery of radio-activity that the process of steadily refining our methods of measurement inaugurated a more detailed investigation of these corpuscles or particles; the development was crowned by C. T. R. Wilson's highly ingenious method, which succeeded in taking snap-shots of the track of a single particle and measuring it very accurately by means of stereometric photographs. As far as the measurements go they confirm, in the case of corpuscles, the validity of the same mechanical laws that hold on a large scale, as with planets, etc. Moreover, it was found that neither the molecules nor the atoms are to be considered as the ultimate building stones of matter, but that the atom itself is an extremely complicated composite system. Definite ideas were formed of the way in which atoms are composed of corpuscles, leading to models that closely resembled the celestial planetary system.

And it was natural that in the theoretical construction of these tiny systems the attempt was at first made to use the same laws of motion as had been so successfully proved to hold good on a large scale. In other words, we endeavored to conceive the "inner" life of the atoms in terms of Hamiltonian mechanics, which, as I have said, have their culmination in the Hamiltonian principle. Meanwhile the very close analogy between the latter and Fermat's optical principle had been almost entirely forgotten. Or if any thought were given to this at all, the analogy was looked upon as merely a curious feature of the mathematical theory of the subject.

Now it is very difficult, without going closely into details, to give a correct notion of the success or failure encountered in the attempt to explain the structure of matter by this picture of the atom which was based on classical mechanics. On the one hand the Hamiltonian principle directly proved itself to be the truest and most reliable guide; so much so as to be considered absolutely indispensable. On the other hand, in order to account for certain facts, one had to tolerate the "rude intrusion" (*groben Eingriff*) of quite new and incomprehensible postulates, which were called quantum conditions and quantum postu-

175

lates. These were gross dissonances in the symphony of classical mechanics—and yet they were curiously chiming in with it, as if they were being played on the same instrument. In mathematical language, the situation may be stated thus: The Hamiltonian principle demands only that a certain integral must be a minimum, without laying down the numerical value of the minimum in this demand; the new postulates require that the numerical value of the minimum must be a whole multiple of a universal constant, which is Planck's Quantum of Action. But this, only in parenthesis. The situation was rather hopeless. If the old mechanics had failed entirely, that would have been tolerable, for thus the ground would have been cleared for a new theory. But as it was, we were faced with the difficult problem of saving its *soul*, whose breath could be palpably detected in this microcosm, and at the same time persuading it, so to speak, not to consider the quantum conditions "rude intruders" but something arising out of the inner nature of the situation itself.

The way out of the difficulty was actually (though unexpectedly) found in the possibility I have already mentioned, namely, that in the Hamiltonian Principle we might also assume the manifestation of a "wave-mechanism," which we supposed to lie at the basis of events in point mechanics, just as we have been long accustomed to acknowledge it in the phenomena of light and in the governing principle enunciated by Fermat. By this, of course, the individual "path" of a mass point absolutely loses its inherent physical significance and becomes something fictitious, just as the individual light ray. Yet the "soul" of the theory, the minimum principle, not only remains inviolate but we could even never reveal its true and simple meaning, as was stated above, *without* introducing the wave theory. The new theory is in reality no *new* theory, but is a thorough organic expansion and development, one might almost say merely a re-statement of the old theory in more subtle terms.

But how could this new and more "subtle" interpretation lead to results that are appreciably different? When applied to the atom, how could it solve any difficulty which the old interpretation could not cope with? How can this new standpoint make that "rude intruder" not merely tolerable but even a welcome guest and part of the household, as it were?

These questions, too, can best be elucidated by reference to the analogy with optics. Although I have asserted, and with good reason, that Fermat's principle is the quintessence of the wave theory of light, yet that principle is not such as to render superfluous a more detailed study of wave processes. The optical phenomena of *diffraction* and *interference* can be understood only when we follow up the particulars of the wave process; because these phenomena depend not merely upon where the wave finally arrives but also on whether at a given moment it arrives there as a wave-crest or a wave-trough. To the older and cruder methods of investigation interference phenomena appeared as only small details and escaped observation. But as soon as they were observed and properly accounted for by means of the undulatory theory, quite a number of experimental devices could be easily arranged in which the undulatory character of light was prominently displayed, not only in the finer details but also in the general character of the experiment.

To explain this I shall bring forward two examples: the first is that of an optical instrument, such as a telescope or a microscope. With such an instrument we aim at obtaining a sharp image. This means that we endeavor to focus all the rays emitted from an object point and re-unite them at what is called the image point (see Fig. 1a). Formerly it was thought that the difficulties which stood in the way were only those of geometrical optics, which are actually very considerable. Later it turned out that even in the best constructed instruments lack of precise focusing was considerably greater than might have been expected if in reality each ray, independently of its neighboring ray, followed Fermat's principle exactly. The light which is emitted from a luminous point and received by an instrument does not focus at an

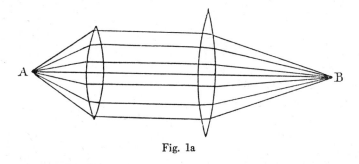

Fig. 1a

exact point after it has passed the instrument. Instead of this, it covers a small circular area, which is called the diffraction image and which is mostly circular only because the diaphragms and the circumference of the lenses are usually circular. For diffraction results from the fact that the instrument cannot possibly receive the whole of the spherical waves

179

which are emitted from a luminous point. The borders of the lenses, and sometimes the diaphragms, cut off a part of the wave surface (Fig. 1b) and—if I may use a somewhat crude expression—the torn edges of the wound prevent an exact focus at a point and bring about the indistinctness or blurring of the image. This

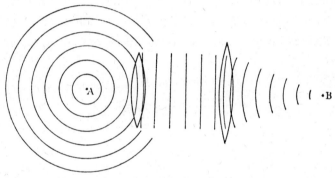

Fig. 1b

blurring is closely connected with the *wave-length* of the light and is absolutely unavoidable, owing to this deep seated theoretical connection. This phenomenon, originally scarcely noticed, now completely governs and inescapably limits the efficiency of the modern microscope, all the other causes of a lack of distinctness in the image having been successfully overcome. With respect to details, which are not much

180

more coarse-grained than the wave-length of light, the optical image can only reach a distant similarity to the original, and none at all whenever the structural details in the object are *finer* than the wave-length.

The second example is of a simpler nature. Let us

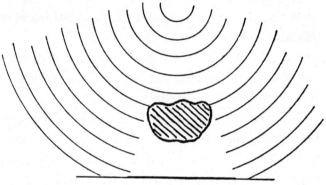

Fig. 5

take a tiny source of light, just a point only. If we place an opaque body between it and a screen we find a shadow thrown on the screen. To construct the shadow theoretically we should follow each ray of light emitted from the point and should ascertain whether the opaque body prevents it from reaching the screen. The *rim* of the shadow is formed by those light rays which just graze and pass by the outline of

181

the opaque body. But it can be shown by experiment that even where the light source is made as minute as possible, and the outline of the opaque body as sharp as possible, the outer rim of the shadow cast by the opaque body on the screen is not really sharp. The cause of this is again the same as in the former example. The wave-front is split, as it were (Fig. 5), by the outline of the opaque body; and the traces of this lesion blur the rim of the shadow. This would be inexplicable if the individual light rays were independent in themselves and traveled independently with no reference to one another.

This phenomenon, which is also called *diffraction*, is generally speaking not very noticeable where larger bodies are concerned. But if the opaque body which throws the shadow be very small, at least in one dimension, then the diffraction has two effects, first, nothing like a true shadow is produced and, secondly —which is far more striking—the tiny body seems to be glowing with its own light and emitting rays in all directions (predominantly, however, at very narrow angles with the incoming rays). Everybody is familiar with the so-called "motes" that appear in the track of a sunbeam entering a dark room. In the same way the filigree of tiny strands and cobwebs that appear around the brow of a hill behind which the sun is hidden, or even the hair of a person standing against the sun, sometimes glows marvelously with diffracted light. The visibility of smoke and fog is due to the same phenomenon. In all these cases the light does not really issue from the opaque body itself but from its immediate surroundings, that is to say, from the area in which the body produces a considerable perturbation of the incident wave-fronts. It is interesting, and for what follows very important, to note that the area of perturbation is always and in every direction at least as large as one or a few wave-lengths, no matter how small the opaque body may be. Here again, therefore, we see the close relation between wave-length and the phenomenon of diffraction. Perhaps this can be more palpably illustrated by reference to another wave process, namely, that of sound. Here, on account of the much longer wave-length, which extends into centimeters and meters, the shadow loses all distinctness and the diffraction predominates to a degree that is of practical importance. We can distinctly *hear* a call from behind a high wall or around the corner of a solid building, although we cannot *see* the person who calls.

Let us now return from optics to mechanics and

try to develop the analogy fully. The optical parallel of the *old* mechanics is the method of dealing with isolated rays of light, which are supposed not to influence one another. The new wave mechanics has its parallel in the undulatory theory of light. The advantage of changing from the old concept to the new must obviously consist in clearer insight into diffraction phenomena, or rather into something that is strictly analogous to the diffraction of light, although ordinarily even less significant; for otherwise the old mechanics could not have been accepted as satisfactory for so long a time. But it is not difficult to conjecture the conditions in which the neglected phenomenon must become very prominent, entirely dominate the mechanical process and present problems that are insoluble under the old concept. This occurs inevitably *whenever the entire mechanical system is comparable in its extension with the wave-lengths of "material waves,"* which play the same rôle in mechanical processes as light waves do in optics.

That is the reason why, in the tiny system of the atom, the old concept is bound to fail. In mechanical phenomena on a large scale it will retain its validity as an excellent approximation, but it must be replaced by the new concept if we wish to deal with the fine interplay which takes place within regions of the order of magnitude of only one or a few wave-lengths. It was amazing to see all the strange additional postulates, which I have mentioned, arising quite automatically from the new undulatory concept, whereas they had to be artificially grafted onto the old one in order to make it fit in with the internal processes of the atom and yield a tolerable explanation of its actually observed manifestations.

In this connection it is, of course, of outstanding importance that the diameter of the atom and the wavelength of these hypothetical "material" waves should be very nearly of the same order of magnitude. And you will undoubtedly ask whether we are to consider it as purely an accident that in the progressive analysis of the structure of matter we should just here encounter the wave-length order of magnitude, or whether this can be explained. Is there any further evidence of the equality in question? Since the material waves are an entirely new requisite of this theory, which had not been hitherto discerned elsewhere, one might suspect that it is merely a question of suitable *assumption* as to their wave-length, an assumption forced upon us in order to support the preceding arguments.

Well, the coincidence between the two orders of magnitude is by no means a mere accident, and there is no necessity to make any particular assumption in this regard; the coincidence follows naturally from the theory, on account of the following remarkable circumstances. Let us begin by stating that Rutherford's and Chadwick's experiments on the dispersion of Alpha rays have firmly established the fact that the heavy *nucleus* of the atom is very much smaller than the atom, which justifies us in treating it as a point-like center of attraction in all the argument which follows. Instead of the *electron* we introduce hypothetical waves, the wave-length of which is left an open question as yet, because we do not know anything about it. It is true that this introduces into our calculations a symbol, say a, which represents a number as yet undefined. But in such calculations we are accustomed to that sort of thing and it does not hinder us from inferring that the nucleus of the atom will inevitably produce a sort of diffraction phenomenon of these waves, just as a minute mote does with light waves. Precisely as with light waves, here too the extension of the perturbed area surrounding the nucleus turns out to bear a close relation to the wave-length and to be of the same order of magnitude.

186

Remember that the latter had to be left an open question! But now comes the most important step: *we identify the perturbed area, the diffraction halo, with the atom; the atom being thus regarded as really nothing more than the diffraction phenomenon arising from an electron wave that has been intercepted by the nucleus of the atom.* Thus it is no longer an accident that the size of the atom is of the same order of magnitude as the wave-length. It is in the nature of the case itself. Of course numerically we know neither the one nor the other; because in our calculation there always remains this *one* undefined constant which we have called *a*. It can, however, be determined in two ways, which control one another reciprocally. Either we can choose for *a* that value which will quantitatively account for the observable effects produced by the atom, especially for the emitted spectral lines, which can be measured with extreme accuracy; or, in the second place, the value of *a* can be adapted in order to give to the diffraction halo the right size, which from other evidence is to be expected for the atom. These two ways of defining *a* (of which the second is, of course, much less definite, because the phrase "size of the atom" is somewhat indefinite) are *in perfect accord with one another*. Thirdly, and finally, it may be remarked that the constant which has remained indeterminate has not really the physical dimension of Length, but of Action, that is, energy multiplied by time. It is, then, very tempting to assign to it the numerical value of Planck's universal Quantum of Action, which is known with fair accuracy from the laws of heat radiation. The result is that with all desirable exactitude, *we now fall back upon the first (the most exact) method of determining* a.

Thus, from the quantitative point of view, the theory answers its purpose with a minimum of new assumptions. It involves a single available constant, to which we only have to assign a numerical value that is already quite familiar to us in the earlier Quantum Theory, in order, first, to give the proper magnitude to the diffraction halos and therewith render possible their identification with the atoms; and, secondly, to calculate with quantitative exactitude all the observable effects produced by the atoms, their radiation of light, the energy required for ionization, etc., etc.

I have tried to explain to you in the simplest possible manner the fundamental concept on which this wave theory of matter is based. Let me confess that, in order to avoid bringing the subject before you in an abstruse form at the very outset, I have embellished it somewhat. Not indeed as regards the thoroughness with which conclusions properly deduced from the theory have been corroborated by experiment, but rather as regards the conceptual simplicity and absence of difficulty in the chain of reasoning which lead to these conclusions. In saying this I do not refer to the mathematical difficulties, which eventually are always trivial, but rather to the conceptual difficulties. Naturally it does not call for a great mental effort to pass from the idea of a path to a system of wave-fronts perpendicular to the path (see

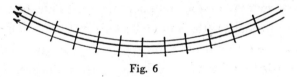

Fig. 6

Fig. 6). But the wave-surfaces, even when we restrict them to small elements of surface, still involve at least a slender *bundle* of possible paths, to all of which they stand in the same relation. According to the traditional idea, in each concrete case one of these paths is singled out as the one "really traveled," in contradistinction to all the other "merely possible" paths. According to the new concept the case is quite different. We are confronted with the profound logical antithesis between

> *Either this or that* (Particle Mechanics)
> (*aut — aut*)
> **and**
> *This as well as that* (Wave Mechanics)
> (*et — et*)

Now this would not be so perplexing if it were really a question of abandoning the old concept and *substituting* the new one for it. But unfortunately that is not the state of affairs. From the standpoint of wave mechanics the innumerable multitude of possible particle paths would be only fictitious and no single one would have the special prerogative of being that actually traveled in the individual case. But, as I have already remarked, we have in some cases actually observed such individual tracks of a particle. The wave theory cannot meet this case, except in a very unsatisfactory way. We find it extraordinarily difficult to regard the track, whose trace we actually *see*, only as a slender bundle of equally possible (*Gleichberechtigten*) tracks between which the wave-fronts form a lateral connection. And yet these lateral connections are necessary to the understanding of diffraction and interference phenomena, which the very same particles produce before our eyes with equal obviousness—that is to say, produce experimentally on a large scale and not only in those concepts of the interior of the atom discussed previously. It is true that we can deal with every concrete individual case without the two contrasted aspects leading to different expectations as to the result of any given experiment. But with the old and cherished and apparently indispensable concepts, such as "really" and "merely possible," we cannot advance. We can never say what really *is* or what really *happens*, but only what is *observable*, in each concrete case. Shall we content ourselves with this as a permanent feature? In principle, yes. It is by no means a new demand to claim that, in principle, the ultimate aim of exact science must be restricted to the description of what is really observable. The question is only whether we must henceforth forgo connecting the description, as we did hitherto, with a definite hypothesis as to the real structure of the Universe. To-day there is a widespread tendency to insist on this renunciation. But I think that this is taking the matter somewhat too lightly.

I would describe the present state of our knowledge

as follows: The light ray, or track of the particle, corresponds to a *longitudinal* continuity of the propagating process (that is to say, *in the* direction of the spreading); the wave-front, on the other hand, to a *transverse* one, that is to say, perpendicular to the direction of spreading. *Both* continuities are undoubtedly real. The one has been proved by photographing the particle tracks, and the other by interference experiments. As yet we have not been able to bring the two together into a uniform scheme. It is only in extreme cases that the transverse—the spherical—continuity or the longitudinal—the ray-continuity shows itself so predominantly that we *believe* we can avail ourselves either of the wave scheme or of the particle scheme alone.

WHAT IS AN ELEMENTARY
PARTICLE?

1. A PARTICLE IS NOT AN INDIVIDUAL

ATOMISM in its latest form is called quantum mechanics. It has extended its range to comprise, besides ordinary matter, all kinds of radiation, including light—in brief, all forms of energy, ordinary matter being one of them. In the present form of the theory the 'atoms' are electrons, protons, photons, mesons, etc. The generic name is elementary particle, or merely particle. The term atom has very wisely been retained for chemical atoms, though it has become a misnomer.

This essay deals with the elementary particle, more particularly with a certain feature that this concept has acquired—or rather lost—in quantum mechanics. I mean this: that the elementary particle is not an individual; it cannot be identified, it lacks 'sameness.' The fact is known to every physicist, but is rarely given any prominence in surveys readable by non-specialists. In technical language it is covered by saying that the particles 'obey' a new-fangled statistics, either Einstein-Bose or Fermi-Dirac statistics. The implication, far from obvious, is that the unsuspected epithet 'this' is not quite properly applicable to, say, an electron, except with caution, in a restricted sense, and sometimes not at all. My objective here is to explain this point and to give it the thought it deserves. In order to create a foil for the discussion, let me summarize in sections 2-5 what we are usually told about particles and waves in the new physics.

2. CURRENT VIEWS: THE AMALGAMATION OF PARTICLES AND WAVES

Our image of the material world had been made up of two kinds of 'fittings': waves and particles. The former were instanced mainly, if not exclusively, by

Maxwell's waves of electromagnetic energy, comprising such as are used in radio, light, X-rays, and gamma-rays. Material bodies were said to consist of particles. One was also familiar with jets of particles, called corpuscular rays, such as cathode rays, beta-rays, alpha-rays, anode rays, etc. Particles would emit and absorb waves. For instance, cathode rays (electrons), when slowed down by colliding with atoms, emit X-rays. The distinction between particles and waves was, however, considered as clear-cut as that between a violin and its sound. An examinee who alleged cathode rays to be waves, or X-rays to be jets of particles, would have got very bad marks.

In the new setting of ideas the distinction has vanished, because it was discovered that all particles have also wave properties, and *vice versa*. Neither of the two concepts must be discarded, they must be amalgamated. Which aspect obtrudes itself depends not on the physical object, but on the experimental device set up to examine it. A jet of cathode rays, for example, produces in a Wilson cloud chamber discrete tracks of water droplets—curved tracks if there is a magnetic field to deflect the electrons, otherwise straight alignments of droplets. We cannot but interpret them as traces of the paths of single electrons. Yet the same jet, after crossing a narrow tube placed at right angles to it and containing crystal powder, will produce on a photographic plate at some distance behind the tube a pattern of concentric circles. This pattern can be understood in all its details when looked upon as the interference pattern of waves, and in no other way. Indeed, it bears a close resemblance to similarly produced X-ray patterns.

The suspicion arises: are the conical jets that impinge on the photographic plate and form the pattern of circles really cathode rays; are they not perhaps secondary X-rays? The suspicion has to be dismissed, for the whole system of circles can be displaced by a magnet, while X-rays can not; moreover, by putting a lead screen with a small hole in it in the place of the photographic plate, a jetlet can be isolated from one of the conical jets and made to display any of the typical particle characters of cathode rays: it will produce discrete tracks in a cloud chamber; bring about discrete discharges in a Geiger-Müller counter; and charge up a Faraday cage in which it is intercepted.

A vast amount of experimental evidence clinches the conviction that wave characteristics and particle characteristics are never encountered singly, but always in a union; they form different aspects of the same phenomenon, and indeed of all physical phenomena. The union is not a loose or superficial one. It would be quite unsatisfactory to consider cathode rays to consist both of particles and of waves. In the early days of the new theory it was suggested that the particles might be singular spots within the waves, actually singularities in the meaning of the mathematician. The white crests on a moderately rough sea would be a fairly adequate simile. The idea was very soon abandoned. It seems that both concepts, that of waves and that of particles, have to be modified considerably, so as to attain a true amalgamation.

3. CURRENT VIEWS: THE NATURE OF WAVES

The waves, so we are told, must not be regarded as quite real waves. It is true that they produce interference patterns—which is the crucial test that in the case of light had removed all doubts as to the reality of the waves. However, we are now told that all waves, including light, ought rather to be looked upon as 'probability waves.' They are only a mathematical device for computing the probability of finding a particle in certain conditions, for instance (in the above example), the probability of an electron hitting the photographic plate within a small specified area. There it is registered by acting on a grain of silver bromide. The interference pattern is to be regarded as a statistical registration of the impinging electrons. The waves are in this context sometimes referred to as guiding waves—guiding or directing the particles on their paths. The guidance is not to be regarded as a rigid one; it merely constitutes a probability. The clear-cut pattern is a statistical result, its definiteness being due to the enormous number of particles.

Here I cannot refrain from mentioning an objection which is too obvious not to occur to the reader. Something that influences the physical behaviour of something else must not in any respect be called less real than the something it influences—whatever meaning we may give to the dangerous epithet 'real.' It is certainly useful to recall at times that all quantitative models or images conceived by the physicist are, epistemologically, only mathematical devices for computing observable events, but I cannot see that this applies more to, say, light-waves than to, say, oxygen molecules.

4. CURRENT VIEWS: THE NATURE OF PARTICLES (UNCERTAINTY RELATION)

As regards the modification required in the concept of a particle, the stress is on Heisenberg's uncertainty relation. The so-called classical mechanics hinged on Galileo's and Newton's discovery that the thing which in a moving body is determined at any instant by the other bodies in its environment is only and precisely its acceleration, or, in mathematical terms, the second derivatives with respect to time of the co-ordinates. The first derivatives, commonly called the velocity, are therefore to be included in the description of the momentary state of the body, together with the co-ordinates themselves which label its momentary place in space or 'whereness' (or ubiety, to use an antiquated but convenient word). Thus, to describe the momentary state of a particle, two independent data were required: its co-ordinates and their first time derivatives, or ubiety and velocity. According to the new theory less is required, and less is obtainable. Either of the two data can be given with arbitrary accuracy, provided that no store is set on the other, but both cannot be known together with absolute precision. One may not even conceive of both as having absolutely sharp values

199

at the same instant. They mutually blur each other, as it were. Broadly speaking, the product of the latitudes of their respective inaccuracies cannot be reduced below a fixed constant. For an electron, this constant happens to be about 1 if the units centimetre and second are used. Thus, if the velocity of an electron is considered sharp with a latitude of only 1 cm/sec, its location has to be considered as blurred within the latitude of 1 cm. The strangeness does not lie in the mere existence of inaccuracies, for the particle might be a thing of vague and changeable extension, within which slightly different velocities prevailed at different spots. Then, however, a sharp location or ubiety would probably entail a sharply defined velocity and *vice versa*. Actually it is just the other way round.

5. CURRENT VIEWS: THE MEANING OF THE UNCERTAINTY RELATION

Two links connect this strange and certainly very fundamental statement to other parts of the theory. It can be arrived at by declaring that a particle is equivalent to its guiding wave, and has no characteristics save those indicated by the guiding wave according to a certain code. The code is simple enough. The ubiety is indicated by the extension of the wave, the latitude in the velocity by the range of wave numbers. 'Wave number' is short for reciprocal of the wavelength. Each wave number corresponds to a certain velocity proportional to it. That is the code. It is a mathematical truism that the smaller a wave group, the wider is the (minimum) spread of its wave numbers.

Alternatively, we may scrutinize the experimental procedure for determining either the ubiety or the velocity. Any such measuring device implies a transfer of energy between the particle and some measuring instrument—eventually the observer himself, who has to take a reading. This means an actual physical interference with the particle. The disturbance cannot be arbitrarily reduced, because energy is not exchanged continuously but in portions. We are given to understand that, when measuring one of the two items, ubiety or velocity, we interfere with the other the more violently the higher the precision we aim at. We blur its value within a latitude inversely proportional to the latitude of error allowed in the first.

In both explanations the wording seems to suggest that the uncertainty or lack of precision refers to the attainable knowledge about a particle rather than to its nature. Indeed, by saying that we disturb or change a measurable physical quantity we logically imply that it has certain values before and after our interference, whether we know them or not. And in the first explanation, involving the wave, if we call it a guiding wave how should it guide the particle on its path, if the particle has not got a path? If we say the wave indicates the probability of finding the particle at A, or at B, or at C . . . this seems to imply that the particle is at one, and one only, of these places; and similarly for the velocity. (Actually the wave does indicate both probabilities simultaneously, one by its extension, the other by its wave numbers.) However, the current view does not accept either ubiety or velocity as permanent objective realities. It stresses the word 'finding.' Finding the particle at point A does not imply that it has been there before. We are more or less given to understand that our measuring device has brought it there or 'concentrated' it at that point, while at the same time we have disturbed its velocity. And this does not imply that the velocity 'had' a value. We have only disturbed or changed the probability of finding this or that value of the velocity if we measure it. The implications as to 'being' or 'having'

202

are misconceptions, to be blamed on language. Positivist philosophy is invoked to tell us that we must not distinguish between the knowledge we can obtain of a physical object and its actual state. The two are one.

6. CRITICISM OF THE UNCERTAINTY RELATION

I will not discuss heré that tenet of positivist philosophy. I fully agree that the uncertainty relation has nothing to do with incomplete knowledge. It does reduce the amount of information attainable about a particle as compared with views held previously. The conclusion is that these views were wrong and we must give them up. We must not believe that the completer description they demanded about what is really going on in the physical world is conceivable, but in practice unobtainable. This would mean clinging to the old view. Still, it does not necessarily follow that we must give up speaking and thinking in terms of what is really going on in the physical world. It has become a convenient habit to picture it as a reality. In everyday life we all follow this habit, even those philosophers who opposed it theoretically, such as Bishop Berkeley. Such theoretical controversy is on a different plane.

Physics has nothing to do with it. Physics takes its start from everyday experience, which it continues by more subtle means. It remains akin to it, does not transcend it generically, it cannot enter into another realm. Discoveries in physics cannot in themselves—so I believe—have the authority of forcing us to put an end to the habit of picturing the physical world as a reality.

I believe the situation is this. We have taken over from previous theory the idea of a particle and all the technical language concerning it. This idea is inadequate. It constantly drives our mind to ask for information which has obviously no significance. Its imaginative structure exhibits features which are alien to the real particle. An adequate picture must not trouble us with this disquieting urge; it must be incapable of picturing more than there is; it must refuse any further addition. Most people seem to think that no such picture can be found. One may, of course, point to the circumstantial evidence (which I am sorry to say is not changed by this essay) that in fact none has been found. I can, however, think of some reasons for this, apart from the genuine intricacy of the case. The palliative, taken from positivist philosophy and purporting to be a reasonable way out, was administered fairly early and authoritatively. It seemed to relieve us from the search for what I should call real understanding; it even rendered the endeavour suspect, as betraying an unphilosophical mind—the mind of a child who regretted the loss of its favourite toy (the picture or model) and would not realize that it was gone for ever. As a second point, I submit that the difficulty may be intimately connected with the principal subject of this paper, to which I shall now turn without further delay. The uncertainty relation refers to the particle. The particle, as we shall see, is not an identifiable individual. It may indeed well be that no individual entity can be conceived which would answer the requirements of the adequate picture stated above.

It is not at all easy to realize this lack of individuality and to find words for it. A symptom is that the probability interpretation, unless it is expressed in the most highly technical language of mathematics, seems to be vague as to whether the wave gives information about one particle or about an *ensemble* of particles. It is not always quite clear whether it indicates the probability of finding 'the' particle or of finding 'a' particle, or indicates the likely or average number of particles in, say, a given small volume. Moreover the most popular view on probability tends to obliterate these differences. It is true that exact mathematical tools are available to distinguish between them. A point of general interest is involved, which I will explain. A method of dealing with the problem of many particles was indicated in 1926 by the present writer. The method uses waves in many-dimensional space, in a manifold of $3N$ dimensions, N being the number of particles. Deeper insight led to its improvement. The step leading to this improvement is of momentous significance. The many-dimensional treatment has been superseded by so-called second quantization, which is mathematically equivalent to uniting into one three-dimensional formulation the cases $N = 0, 1, 2, 3 \ldots$ (to infinity) of the many-dimensional treatment. This highly ingenious device includes the so-called new statistics, with which we shall have to deal below in much simpler terms. It is the only precise formulation of the views now held, and the one that is always used. What is so very significant in our present context is that one cannot avoid leaving indeterminate the number of the particles dealt with. It is thus obvious that they are not individuals.

7. THE NOTION OF A PIECE OF MATTER

I wish to set forth a view on matter and the material universe, to which Ernst Mach [1], Bertrand Russell ([2], and others were led by a careful analysis of concepts. It differs from the popular view. We are, however, not concerned with the psychological origin of the concept of matter but with its epistemological analysis. The attitude is so simple that it can hardly claim complete novelty; some pre-Socratics, including the materialist Democritus [3], were nearer to it than were the great men who resuscitated science and moulded it during the seventeenth to nineteenth centuries.

According to this view, a piece of matter is the name we give to a continuous string of events that succeed each other in time, immediately successive ones being as a rule closely similar. The single event is an inextricable complex of sensates, of associated memory images, and of expectations associated with the former two. The sensates prevail in the case of an unknown object, say a distant white patch on the road, which might be a stone, snow, salt, a cat or a dog, a white shirt or blouse, a handkerchief. Even so, within the ensuing string of events we usually know from general experience how to discount the changes caused by motions of our own body, in particular of our direction of sight. As soon as the nature of the object is recognized, images and expectations begin to prevail. The latter concern sensations as hard, soft, heavy, flexible, rough, smooth, cold, salty, etc., associated with the image of touching and handling; they also concern spontaneous movements or noises such as barking, mewing, shouting, etc. It should be noted that I am not speaking of our thoughts or considerations about the object, but of what forms part and parcel of our perception of it— of what it is to us. However, the limit is not sharp. As our familiarity with a piece of matter grows, and in particular as we approach its scientific aspect, the range of expectations in regard to it widens, eventually to include all the information science has ascertained, e.g. melting point, solubility, electric conductivity, density, chemical and crystalline structure, and so on. At the same time, the momentary sensational core recedes in relevance the more the object becomes familiar to us, whether by scientific knowledge or by everyday use.

8. INDIVIDUALITY OR 'SAMENESS'

After a certain wealth of association has come to

208

outshine the core of sensates, the latter is no longer needed to keep the complex together. It persists even when the contact of our senses with the object temporarily ceases. And more than that: the complex is latently conserved even when the whole string is interrupted by our turning away from the object to others and forgetting all about it. Indeed, this is not exceptional, but a rule which—since we sometimes sleep—has no exception. But we have adopted the useful device of filling these gaps. We supplement the missing parts of the strings relating to pieces of matter in our nearer and farther surroundings, to cover the periods when we neither watch them nor think of them. When a familiar object re-enters our ken, it is usually recognized as a continuation of previous appearances, as being the same thing. The relative permanence of individual pieces of matter is the most momentous feature of both everyday life and scientific experience. If a familiar article, say an earthenware jug, disappears from your room, you are quite sure somebody must have taken it away. If after a time it reappears, you may doubt whether it really is the same one—breakable objects in such circumstances are often not. You may not be able to decide the issue, but you will have no doubt that the

209

doubtful sameness has an indisputable meaning—
that there is an unambiguous answer to your query.
So firm is our belief in the continuity of the unob-
served parts of the strings!

No doubt the notion of individuality of pieces of
matter dates from time immemorial. I suppose animals must have it in some way, and a dog, when
seeking for his ball that has been hidden, displays
it very plainly. Science has taken it over as a matter
of course. It has refined it so as safely to embrace
all cases of apparent disappearance of matter. The
idea that a log which burns away first turns into fire,
then into ashes and smoke, is not alien to the primitive mind. Science has substantiated it; though the
appearance in bulk may change, the ultimate constituents of the matter do not. This was (in spite of
his occasional scepticism mentioned above) the
teaching of Democritus. Neither he nor Dalton
doubted that an atom which was originally present
in the block of wood is afterwards either in the ashes
or in the smoke.

9. THE BEARING ON ATOMISM

In the new turn of atomism that began with the
papers of Heisenberg and of de Broglie in 1925 such

an attitude has to be abandoned. This is the most startling revelation emerging from the ensuing development, and the feature which in the long run is bound to have the most important consequences. If we wish to retain atomism we are forced by observed facts to deny the ultimate constituents of matter the character of identifiable individuals. Up to recently, atomists of all ages, for all I know, had transferred that characteristic from visible and palpable pieces of matter to the atoms, which they could not see or touch or observe singly. Now we do observe single particles; we see their tracks in the cloud chamber and in photographic emulsions; we register the practically simultaneous discharges caused by a single swift particle in two or three Geiger counters placed at several yards' distance from each other. Yet we must deny the particle the dignity of being an absolutely identifiable individual. Formerly, if a physicist were asked what stuff the atoms themselves were made of, he might smile and shirk the answer. If the inquirer insisted on the question whether he might imagine them as small unchangeable bits of ordinary matter, he would get the smiling reply that there was no point in doing so but that it would do no harm. The formerly meaningless question has now gained significance. The answer is definitely in the negative. An atom lacks the most primitive property we associate with a piece of matter in ordinary life. Some philosophers of the past, if the case could be put to them, would say that the modern atom consists of no stuff at all but is pure shape.

10. THE MEANING OF THE NEW STATISTICS

We must at last proceed to give the reasons for this change of attitude in a more comprehensible form than at the end of section 6. It rests on the so-called new statistics. There are two of them. One is the Bose-Einstein statistics, whose novelty and relevance were first stressed by Einstein. The other is the Fermi-Dirac statistics, of which the most pregnant expression is Pauli's exclusion principle. I shall try to explain the new statistics, and its relation to the old classical or Boltzmann statistics, to those who have never heard about such things and perhaps may be puzzled by what 'statistics' means in the context. I shall use an instance from everyday life. It may seem childishly simple, particularly because we have to choose small numbers—actually 2 and 3—in order to make the arithmetic surveyable. Apart from this, the illustration is completely adequate and covers the actual situation.

212

Three schoolboys, Tom, Dick, and Harry, deserve a reward. The teacher has two rewards to distribute among them. Before doing so, he wishes to realize for himself how many different distributions are at all possible. This is the only question we investigate (we are not interested in his eventual decision). It is a statistical question: to count the number of different distributions. The point is that the answer depends on the nature of the rewards. Three different kinds of reward will illustrate the three kinds of statistics.

(a) The two rewards are two memorial coins with portraits of Newton and Shakespeare respectively. The teacher may give Newton either to Tom or to Dick or to Harry, and Shakespeare either to Tom or to Dick or to Harry. Thus there are three times three, that is nine, different distributions (classical statistics).

(b) The two rewards are two shilling-pieces (which, for our purpose, we must regard as indivisible quantities). They can be given to two different boys, the third going without. In addition to these three possibilities there are three more: either Tom or Dick or Harry receives two shillings. Thus there are six different distributions (Bose-Einstein statistics).

(*c*) The two rewards are two vacancies in the football team that is to play for the school. In this case two boys can join the team, and one of the three is left out. Thus there are three different distributions (Fermi-Dirac statistics).

Let me mention right away the *rewards* represent the particles, two of the same kind in every case; the boys represent states the particle can assume. Thus, 'Newton is given to Dick' means: the particle Newton takes on the state Dick.

Notice that the counting is natural, logical, and indisputable in every case. It is uniquely determined by the nature of the objects: memorial coins, shillings, memberships. They are of different categories. Memorial coins are individuals distinguished from one another. Shillings, for all intents and purposes, are not, but they are still capable of being owned in the plural. It makes a difference whether you have one shilling, or two, or three. There is no point in two boys exchanging their shillings. It does change the situation, however, if one boy gives up his shilling to another. With memberships, neither has a meaning. You can either belong to a team or not. You cannot belong to it twice over.

Experimental evidence proves that statistical counts referring to elementary particles must never follow the pattern (a), but must follow either (b) or (c). Some hold that for all genuinely elementary particles (c) is competent. Such particles, electrons for instance, correspond to membership in a club; I mean to the abstract notion of membership, not to the members. Any person eligible to membership in that club represents a well-defined state an electron can take on. If the person is a member, that means there is an electron in that particular state. According to Pauli's exclusion principle, there can never be more than one electron in a particular state. Our simile renders this by declaring double membership meaningless—as in most clubs it would be. In the course of time the list of members changes, and membership is now attached to other persons: the electrons have gone over into other states. Whether you can, in a loose way, speak of a certain membership going over from Dick to Tom, thence from Tom to Harry, etc., depends on the circumstances. They may suggest this view, or they may not, but never in an absolute fashion. In this our simile is perfect, for it

215

is the same with an electron. Moreover, it is quite appropriate to consider the number of members as fluctuating. Indeed, electrons too are created and annihilated.

The example may seem odd and inverted. One might think, 'Why cannot the people be the electrons and various clubs their states? That would be so much more natural.' The physicist regrets, but he cannot oblige. And this is just the salient point: the actual statistical behaviour of electrons cannot be illustrated by any simile that represents them by identifiable things. That is why it follows from their actual statistical behaviour that they are not identifiable things.

The case (b), illustrating Einstein-Bose statistics, is competent for light quanta. (photons), *inter alia*. It hardly needs discussion. It does not strike us as so strange for the very reason that it includes light, i.e. electro-magnetic energy; and energy, in prequantum times, had always been thought of in very much the way our simile represents it, viz. as having quantity, but no individuality.

11. RESTRICTED NOTION OF IDENTITY

The most delicate question is that of the states of, say, an electron. They are, of course, to be defined

216

not classically, but in the light of the uncertainty relation. The rigorous treatment referred to at the end of section 6 is not really based on the notion of 'state of one electron' but on that of 'state of the assembly of electrons.' The whole list of members of the club, as it were, has to be envisaged together—or rather several membership lists, corresponding to the several kinds of particles that go to compose the physical system under consideration. I mention this, not to go into details about it, but because, taken rigorously, the club simile has two flaws. First, the possible states of an electron (which we had assimilated to the persons eligible for membership) are not absolutely defined; they depend on the arrangement of the—actual or imagined—experiment. Given this arrangement, the states are well-defined individuals, which the electrons are not. They also form—and this is the second flaw of the simile—a well-ordered manifold. That is, there is a meaning in speaking of neighbouring states as against such as are farther remote from each other. Moreover, I believe it is true to say that this order can be conceived in such a fashion that, as a rule, whenever one occupied state ceases to be occupied, a neighbouring state becomes occupied.

217

This explains that, in favourable circumstances, long strings of successively occupied states may be produced, similar to those contemplated in sections 7 and 8. Such a string gives the impression of an identifiable individual, just as in the case of any object in our daily surrounding. It is in this way that we must look upon the tracks in the cloud chamber or in a photographic emulsion, and on the (practically) simultaneous discharges of Geiger counters set in a line, which discharges we say are caused by the same particle passing one counter after another. In such cases it would be extremely inconvenient to discard this terminology. There is, indeed, no reason to ban it, provided we are aware that, on sober experimental grounds, the sameness of a particle is not an absolute concept. It has only a restricted significance and breaks down completely in some cases.

In what circumstances this restricted sameness will manifest itself is fairly obvious; namely, when only few states are occupied in the region of the state-manifold with which we are concerned, or, in other words, when the occupied states are not too crowded in that region, or when occupation is a rare event—the terms few, crowded, and rare all referring to the state-manifold. Otherwise, the strings intermingle inextricably and reveal the true situation. In the last section we shall formulate the quantitative condition for the prevailing of restricted individuality. Now we ask what happens when it is obliterated.

12. CROWDEDNESS AND WAVE ASPECT

One gains the impression that according as the individuality of the particles is wiped out by crowding, the particle aspect becomes altogether less and less expedient and has to be replaced by the wave aspect. For instance, in the electronic shell of an atom or molecule the crowding is extreme, almost all the states within a certain region being occupied by electrons. The same holds for the so-called free electrons inside a metal. Indeed, in both cases the particle aspect becomes entirely incompetent. On the other hand, in an ordinary gas the molecules are extremely rare in the wide region of states over which they spread. No more than one state in 10,000 or so is occupied. And, indeed, the theory of gases, based on the particle aspect, was able to attain great perfection long before the wave nature of ordinary matter was discovered. (In the last remark I have been speaking of the molecules as if they were ultimate particles; this is legitimate as far as their translatory motion is concerned.)

219

It is tempting to assign to the two rivals, the particle aspect and the wave aspect, full competences in the limiting cases of extreme 'rarefaction' and extreme 'crowding' respectively. This would separate them, as it were, with only some sort of transition required for the intermediate region. This idea is not entirely wrong, but it is also far from correct. One may remember the interference patterns referred to in section 2 in evidence of the wave nature of the electron. They can be obtained with an arbitrarily faint bundle of cathode rays, provided the exposure is prolonged. Thus a typical wave phenomenon is produced here, irrespective of crowding. Another instance is this. A competent theoretical investigation of the collision of two particles, whether of the same or of different kind, has to take account of their wave nature. The results are duly applied to the collisions of cosmic ray particles with atomic nuclei in the atmosphere, both being extremely rarefied in every sense of the word. But perhaps this is trivial; it only means that even an isolated particle, which gives us the illusion of transitory individuality, must yet not be likened to a classical particle. It remains subject to the uncertainty relation, of which the only tolerable image is the guiding wave group.

13. THE CONDITION FOR THE PARTICLE ASPECT

The following is the quantitative condition for strings to develop which counterfeit individuals and suggest the particle aspect: the product of the momentum p and the average distance l between neighbouring particles must be fairly large compared with Planck's constant h; thus

$$pl \gg h.$$

(The momentum p—and not the velocity—is the thing we should really have referred to when, in sections 4 and 5, we dealt with the uncertainty relation; p is simply the product of the mass and the velocity, unless the latter is comparable with that of light.)

A large l means a low density in ordinary space. What matters, however, is the density in the manifold of states—or phase space, to use the technical term. That is why the momentum p comes in. It is gratifying to remember that those very obvious strings—visible tracks in the cloud chamber or in the photographic emulsion, and simultaneous discharges of aligned counters—are all produced by particles with comparatively very large momentum.

The above relation is familiar from the theory of gases, where it expresses the condition which must be fulfilled in very good approximation in order that the old classical particle theory of gases should apply in very good approximation. This theory has to be modified according to quantum theory when the temperature is very low and at the same time the density very high, so that the product pl is no longer very large compared with h. This modification is called the theory of degenerate gases, of which the most famous application is that by A. Sommerfeld to the electrons inside a metal; we have mentioned them before as an instance of extreme crowding.

There is the following connection between our relation and the uncertainty relation. The latter allows one at any moment to distinguish a particle from its neighbours by locating it with an error considerably smaller than the average distance l. But this entails an uncertainty in p. On account of it, as the particle moves on, the uncertainty in the location grows. If one demands that it still remain well below l after the particle has covered the distance l, one arrives precisely at the above relation.

But again I must warn of a misconception which the preceding sentences might suggest, viz. that crowding only prevents us from registering the identity of a particle, and that we mistake one particle for the other. The point is that they are not individuals which could be confused or mistaken one for another. Such statements are meaningless.

REFERENCES

[1] MACH, ERNST. 'Erkenntnis und Irrtum,' J. A. Barth, Leipzig. 1905.

[2] RUSSELL, BERTRAND. 'Human Knowledge, Its Scope and Limits,' Allen and Unwin, London. 1948.

[3] DIELS, HERMANN. 'Die Fragmente der Vorsokratiker,' Weidmannsche Buchhandlung, Berlin. 1903. (The reference is mainly to the fragment 125 of Democritus.)

DOVER BOOKS ON SCIENCE
BOOKS THAT EXPLAIN SCIENCE

CONCERNING THE NATURE OF THINGS, Sir William Bragg. Christmas lectures delivered at the Royal Society by Nobel laureate. Why a spinning ball travels in a curved track; how uranium is transmuted to lead, etc. Partial contents: atoms, gases, liquids, crystals, metals etc. No scientific background needed; wonderful for intelligent high school student. 32pp. of photos, 57 figures. xii + 232pp. 5⅜ x 8.   T31 Paperbound **$1.35**

THE NATURE OF LIGHT AND COLOUR IN THE OPEN AIR, M. Minnaert. Why is falling snow sometimes black? What causes mirages, the fata morgana, multiple suns and moons in the sky; how are shadows formed? Prof. Minnaert of the University of Utrecht answers these and similar questions in optics, light, colour, for non-specialists. Particularly valuable to nature, science students, painters, photographers. Translated by H. M. Kremer-Priest, K. Jay. 202 illustrations, including 42 photos. xvi + 362pp. 5⅜ x 8.   T196 Paperbound **$1.95**

THE RESTLESS UNIVERSE, Max Born. New enlarged version of this remarkably readable account by a Noble laureate. Moving from subatomic particles to universe, the author explains in very simple terms the latest theories of wave mechanics. Partial contents: air and its relatives, electrons & ions, waves & particles, electronic structure of the atom, nuclear physics. Nearly 600 illustrations, including 7 animated sequences. 325pp. 6 x 9.   T412 Paperbound **$2.00**

MATTER & LIGHT, THE NEW PHYSICS, L. de Broglie. Non-technical papers by a Nobel laureate explain electromagnetic theory, relativity, matter, light and radiation, wave mechanics, quantum physics, philosophy of science. Einstein, Planck, Bohr, others explained so easily that no mathematical training is needed for all but 2 of the 21 chapters. Unabridged. Index. 300pp. 5⅜ x 8.   T35 Paperbound **$1.75**

THE COMMON SENSE OF THE EXACT SCIENCES, W. K. Clifford. Introduction by James Newman, edited by Karl Pearson. For 70 years this has been a guide to classical scientific and mathematical thought. Explains with unusual clarity basic concepts, such as extension of meaning of symbols, characteristics of surface boundaries, properties of plane figures, vectors, Cartesian method of determining position, etc. Long preface by Bertrand Russell. Bibliography of Clifford. Corrected. 130 diagrams redrawn. 249pp. 5⅜ x 8.   T61 Paperbound **$1.60**

THE EVOLUTION OF SCIENTIFIC THOUGHT FROM NEWTON TO EINSTEIN, A. d'Abro. Einstein's special and general theories of relativity, with their historical implications, are analyzed in non-technical terms. Excellent accounts of the contributions of Newton, Riemann, Weyl, Planck, Eddington, Maxwell, Lorentz and others are treated in terms of space and time, equations of electromagnetics, finiteness of the universe, methodology of science. 21 diagrams. 482pp. 5⅜ x 8.   T2 Paperbound **$2.00**

WHAT IS SCIENCE, Norman Campbell. This excellent introduction explains scientific method, role of mathematics, types of scientific laws. Contents: 2 aspects of science, science & nature, laws of science, discovery of laws, explanation of laws, measurement & numerical laws, applications of science. 192pp. 5⅜ x 8.   S43 Paperbound **$1.25**

THE RISE OF THE NEW PHYSICS, A. d'Abro. A half-million word exposition, formerly titled THE DECLINE OF MECHANISM, for readers not versed in higher mathematics. The only thorough explanation, in everyday language, of the central core of modern mathematical physical theory, treating both classical and modern theoretical physics, and presenting in terms almost anyone can understand the equivalent of 5 years of study of mathematical physics. Scientifically impeccable coverage of mathematical-physical thought from the Newtonian system up through the electronic theories of Dirac and Heisenberg and Fermi's statistics. Combines both history and exposition; provides a broad yet unified and digestible view, with constant comparison of classical and modern views on phenomena and theories. "A must for anyone doing serious study in the physical sciences," **JOURNAL OF THE FRANKLIN INSTITUTE.** "Extraordinary faculty . . . to explain ideas and theories of theoretical physics in the language of daily life," **ISIS.** Indexed. 97 illustrations. ix + 982pp. 5⅜ x 8.
                                                       T3 Volume 1, Paperbound **$2.00**
                                                       T4 Volume 2, Paperbound **$2.00**

A HISTORY OF ASTRONOMY FROM THALES TO KEPLER, J. L. E. Dreyer. (Formerly A HISTORY OF PLANETARY SYSTEMS FROM THALES TO KEPLER.) This is the only work in English to give the complete history of man's cosmological views from prehistoric times to Kepler and Newton. Partial contents: Near Eastern astronomical systems, Early Greeks. Homocentric spheres of Eudoxus, Epicycles. Ptolemaic system, medieval cosmology. Copernicus. Kepler, etc. Revised, foreword by W. H. Stahl. New bibliography. xvii + 430pp. 5⅜ x 8.   S79 Paperbound **$1.98**

THE PSYCHOLOGY OF INVENTION IN THE MATHEMATICAL FIELD, J. Hadamard. Where do ideas come from? What role does the unconscious play? Are ideas best developed by mathematical reasoning, word reasoning, visualization? What are the methods used by Einstein, Poincaré, Galton, Riemann. How can these techniques be applied by others? Hadamard, one of the world's leading mathematicians, discusses these and other questions. xiii + 145pp. 5⅜ x 8.   T107 Paperbound **$1.25**

SPINNING TOPS AND GYROSCOPIC MOTION, John Perry. Well-known classic of science still unsurpassed for lucid, accurate, delightful exposition. How quasi-rigidity is induced in flexible and fluid bodies by rapid motion; why gyrostat falls, top rises; nature and effect on climatic conditions of earth's precessional movement; effect of internal fluidity on rotating bodies, etc. Appendixes describe practical uses to which gyroscopes have been put in ships, compasses, monorail transportation. 62 figures. 128pp. 5⅜ x 8.   T416 Paperbound **$1.00**

A CONCISE HISTORY OF MATHEMATICS, D. Struik. Lucid study of development of mathematical ideas, techniques, from Ancient Near East, Greece, Islamic science, Middle Ages, Renaissance, modern times. Important mathematicians are described in detail. Treatment is not anecdotal, but analytical development of ideas. "Rich in content, thoughtful in interpretation" U. S. QUARTERLY BOOKLIST. Non-technical; no mathematical training needed. Index. 60 illustrations, including Egyptian papyri, Greek mss., portraits of 31 eminent mathematicians. Bibliography. 2nd edition. xix + 299pp. 5⅜ x 8. S255 Paperbound **$1.75**

FOUNDATIONS OF GEOMETRY, Bertrand Russell. Analyzing basic problems in the overlap area between mathematics and philosophy, Nobel laureate Russell examines the nature of geometrical knowledge, the nature of geometry, and the application of geometry to space. It covers the history of non-Euclidean geometry, philosophic interpretations of geometry—especially Kant—projective and metrical geometry. This is most interesting as the solution offered in 1897 by a great mind to a problem still current. New introduction by Prof. Morris Kline of N. Y. University. xii + 201pp. 5⅜ x 8. S232 Clothbound **$3.25**
S233 Paperbound **$1.60**

THE NATURE OF PHYSICAL THEORY, P. W. Bridgman. Here is how modern physics looks to a highly unorthodox physicist—a Nobel laureate. Pointing out many absurdities of science, and demonstrating the inadequacies of various physical theories, Dr. Bridgman weighs and analyzes the contributions of Einstein, Bohr, Newton, Heisenberg, and many others. This is a non-technical consideration of the correlation of science and reality. Index. xi + 138pp. 5⅜ x 8.
S33 Paperbound **$1.25**

EXPERIMENT AND THEORY IN PHYSICS, Max Born. A Nobel laureate examines the nature and value of the counterclaims of experiment and theory in physics. Synthetic versus analytical scientific advances are analyzed in the work of Einstein, Bohr, Heisenberg, Planck, Eddington, Milne, and others by a fellow participant. 44pp. 5⅜ x 8. S308 Paperbound **60c**

THE STUDY OF THE HISTORY OF MATHEMATICS & THE STUDY OF THE HISTORY OF SCIENCE, George Sarton. Scientific method & philosophy in 2 scholarly fields. Defines duty of historian of math provides especially useful bibliography with best available biographies of modern mathematicians, editions of their collected works, correspondence. Shows that combination of history & science will aid scholar in understanding science today. Bibliography includes best known treatises on historical methods. 200-item critically evaluated bibliography. Index. 10 illustrations. 2 volumes bound as one. 113pp. + 75pp. 5⅜ x 8. T240 Paperbound **$1.25**

SCIENCE AND METHOD, Henri Poincaré. Procedure of scientific discovery, methodology, experiment, idea-germination—the intellectual processes by which discoveries come into being. Most significant and most interesting aspects of development, application of ideas. Chapters cover selection of facts, chance, mathematical reasoning, mathematics and logic; Whitehead, Russell, Cantor; the new mechanics, etc. 288pp. 5⅜ x 8. S222 Paperbound **$1.25**

SCIENCE AND HYPOTHESIS, Henri Poincaré. Creative psychology in science. How such concepts as number, magnitude, space, force, classical mechanics were developed, and how the modern scientist uses them in his thought. Hypothesis in physics, theories of modern physics. Introduction by Sir James Larmor. "Few mathematicians have had the breadth of vision of Poincaré, and none is his superior in the gift of clear exposition," E. T. Bell. Index. 272pp. 5⅜ x 8.
S221 Paperbound **$1.25**

FOUNDATIONS OF PHYSICS, R. B. Lindsay & H. Margenau. Excellent bridge between semi-popular works & technical treatises. A discussion of methods of physical description, construction of theory; valuable for physicist with elementary calculus who is interested in ideas that give meaning to data, tools of modern physics. Contents include symbolism, mathematical equations; space & time; foundations of mechanics; probability; physics & continua; electron theory; special & general relativity; quantum mechanics; causality. "Thorough and yet not overdetailed. Unreservedly recommended," NATURE (London). Unabridged, corrected edition. List of recommended readings. 35 illustrations. xi + 537pp. 5⅜ x 8. S377 Paperbound **$2.45**

CLASSICS OF SCIENCE

THE THIRTEEN BOOKS OF EUCLID'S ELEMENTS, edited by **Sir Thomas Heath.** Definitive edition of one of the very greatest classics of Western world. Complete English translation of Heiberg text, together with spurious Book XIV. Detailed 150-page introduction discussing aspects of Greek and medieval mathematics. Euclid, texts, commentators, etc. Paralleling the text is an elaborate critical apparatus analyzing each definition, proposition, postulate, covering textual matters, mathematical analysis, commentators of all times, refutations, supports, extrapolations, etc. This is the full EUCLID. Unabridged reproduction of Cambridge U. 2nd edition. 3 volumes. Total of 995 figures, 1426pp. 5⅜ x 8. S88,89,90 3 volume set, paperbound **$6.00**

OPTICKS, Sir Isaac Newton. In its discussions of light, reflection, color, refraction, theories of wave and corpuscular theories of light, this work is packed with scores of insights and discoveries. In its precise and practical discussion of construction of optical apparatus, contemporary understandings of phenomena it is truly fascinating to modern physicists, astronomers, mathematicians. Foreword by Albert Einstein. Preface by I. B. Cohen of Harvard University. 7 pages of portraits, facsimile pages, letters, etc. cxvi + 414pp. 5⅜ x 8. S205 Paperbound **$2.00**

THE PRINCIPLE OF RELATIVITY, A. Einstein, H. Lorentz, M. Minkowski, H. Weyl. These are the 11 basic papers that founded the general and special theories of relativity, all translated into English. Two papers by Lorentz on the Michelson experiment, electromagnetic phenomena. Minkowski's SPACE & TIME, and Weyl's GRAVITATION & ELECTRICITY. 7 epoch-making papers by Einstein: ELECTROMAGNETICS OF MOVING BODIES, INFLUENCE OF GRAVITATION IN PROPAGATION OF LIGHT, COSMOLOGICAL CONSIDERATIONS, GENERAL THEORY, and 3 others. 7 diagrams. Special notes by A. Sommerfeld. 224pp. 5⅜ x 8. S81 Paperbound **$1.75**

THE ANALYTICAL THEORY OF HEAT, Joseph Fourier. This book, which revolutionized mathematical physics, is listed in the Great Books program, and many other listings of great books. It has been used with profit by generations of mathematicians and physicists who are interested in either heat or in the application of the Fourier integral. Covers cause and reflections of rays of heat, radiant heating, heating of closed spaces, use of trigonometric series in the theory of heat, Fourier integral, etc. Translated by Alexander Freeman. 20 figures. xxii + 466pp. 5⅜ x 8.   S93 Paperbound **$2.00**

THE WORKS OF ARCHIMEDES, edited by **T. L. Heath.** All the known works of the great Greek mathematician are contained in this one volume, including the recently discovered Method of Archimedes. Contains: On Sphere & Cylinder, Measurement of a Circle, Spirals, Concids, Spheroids, etc. This is the definitive edition of the greatest mathematical intellect of the ancient world. 186-page study by Heath discusses Archimides and the history of Greek mathematics. Bibliography. 563pp. 5⅜ x 8.   S9 Paperbound **$2.00**

A PHILOSOPHICAL ESSAY ON PROBABILITIES, Marquis de Laplace. This famous essay explains without recourse to mathematics the principle of probability, and the application of probability to games of chance, natural philosophy, astronomy, many other fields. Translated from the 6th French edition by F. W. Truscott, F. L. Emory, with new introduction for this edition by E. T. Bell. 204pp. 5⅜ x 8.   S166 Paperbound **$1.25**

INVESTIGATIONS ON THE THEORY OF THE BROWNIAN MOVEMENT, Albert Einstein. Reprints from rare European journals. 5 basic papers, including the Elementary Theory of the Brownian Movement, written at the request of Lorentz to provide a simple explanation. Translated by A. D. Cowper. Annotated, edited by R. Fürth. 33pp. of notes elucidate, give history of previous investigations. Author, subject indexes. 62 footnotes. 124pp. 5⅜ x 8.
                                                               S304 Paperbound **$1.25**

THE GEOMETRY OF RENÉ DESCARTES. With this book Descartes founded analytical geometry. Original French text, with Descartes' own diagrams, and excellent Smith-Latham translation. Contains Problems the Construction of Which Requires Only Straight Lines and Circles; On the Nature of Curved Lines; On the Construction of Solid or Supersolid Problems. Notes. Diagrams. 258pp. 5⅜ x 8.   S68 Paperbound **$1.50**

DIALOGUES CONCERNING TWO NEW SCIENCES, Galileo Galilei. This classic of experimental science, mechanics, engineering, is as enjoyable as it is important. Based on 30 years' experimentation and characterized by its author as "superior to everything else of mine," it offers a lively exposition of dynamics, elasticity, sound, ballistics, strength of materials, and the scientific method. Translated by H. Grew and A. de Salvio. 126 diagrams. Index. xxi + 288pp. 5⅜ x 8.   S99 Paperbound **$1.65**

TREATISE ON ELECTRICITY AND MAGNETISM, James Clerk Maxwell. For more than 80 years a seemingly inexhaustible source of leads for physicists, mathematicians, engineers. Total of 1082pp. on such topics as Measurement of Quantities, Electrostatics, Elementary Mathematical Theory of Electricity, Electrical Work and Energy in a System of Conductors, General Theorems, Theory of Electrical Images, Electrolysis, Conduction, Polarization, Dielectrics, Resistance, etc. "The greatest mathematical physicist since Newton," Sir James Jeans. 3rd edition. 107 figures, 21 plates. 1082pp. 5⅜ x 8.   S186 Clothbound **$4.95**

PRINCIPLES OF PHYSICAL OPTICS, Ernst Mach. This classical examination of the propagation of light, color, polarization etc. offers a historical and philosophical treatment that has never been surpassed for breadth and easy readability. Contents: Rectilinear propagation of light. Reflection, refraction. Early knowledge of vision. Dioptrics. Composition of light. Theory of color and dispersion. Periodicity. Theory of interference. Polarization. Mathematical representation of properties of light. Propagation of waves, etc. 279 illustrations, 10 portraits. Appendix. Indexes. 324pp. 5⅜ x 8.   S178 Paperbound **$1.75**

THEORY OF ELECTRONS AND ITS APPLICATION TO THE PHENOMENA OF LIGHT AND RADIANT HEAT, H. Lorentz. Lectures delivered at Columbia University by Nobel laureate Lorentz. Unabridged, they form a historical coverage of the theory of free electrons, motion, absorption of heat, Zeeman effect, propagation of light in molecular bodies, inverse Zeeman effect, optical phenomena in moving bodies, etc. 109 pages of notes explain the more advanced sections. Index. 9 figures. 352pp. 5⅜ x 8.   S173 Paperbound **$1.85**

MATTER & MOTION, James Clerk Maxwell. This excellent exposition begins with simple particles and proceeds gradually to physical systems beyond complete analysis: motion, force, properties of centre of mass of material system, work, energy, gravitation, etc. Written with all Maxwell's original insights and clarity! Notes by E. Larmor. 17 diagrams. 178pp. 5⅜ x 8.
                                                               S188 Paperbound **$1.25**

AN INTRODUCTION TO THE STUDY OF EXPERIMENTAL MEDICINE, Claude Bernard. 90-year-old classic of medical science, only major work of Bernard available in English, records his efforts to transform physiology into exact science. Principles of scientific research illustrated by specific case histories from his work; roles of chance, error, preliminary false conclusions, in leading eventually to scientific truth; use of hypothesis. Much of modern application of mathematics to biology rests on the foundation set down here. New foreword by Professor I. B. Cohen, Harvard Univ. xxv + 266pp. 5⅜ x 8.   T400 Paperbound **$1.50**

PRINCIPLES OF MECHANICS, Heinrich Hertz. This last work by the great 19th century physicist is not only a classic, but of great interest in the logic of science. Creating a new system of mechanics based upon space, time, and mass, it returns to axiomatic analysis, to understanding of the formal or structural aspects of science, taking into account logic, observation, and a priori elements. Of great historical importance to Poincaré, Carnap, Einstein, Milne. A 20-page introduction by R. S. Cohen, Wesleyan University, analyzes the implications of Hertz's thought and the logic of science. Bibliography. 13-page introduction of Helmholtz. xiii + 274pp. 5⅜ x 8.
S316 Clothbound **$3.50**
S317 Paperbound **$1.75**

ANIMALS IN MOTION, Eadweard Muybridge. Largest, most comprehensive selection of Muybridge's famous action photos of animals, from his ANIMAL LOCOMOTION. 3919 high-speed shots of 34 different animals and birds in 123 different types of action: horses, mules, oxen, pigs, goats, camels, elephants, dogs, cats, guanacos, sloths, lions, tigers, jaguars, raccoons, baboons, deer, elk, gnus, kangaroos, many others, in different actions—walking, running, flying, leaping. Horse alone shown in more than 40 different ways. Photos taken against ruled backgrounds; most actions taken from 3 angles at once: 90°, 60°, rear. Most plates original size. Of considerable interest to scientists as a classic of biology, as a record of actual facts of natural history and physiology. "A really marvellous series of plates," NATURE (London). "A monumental work," Waldemar Kaempffert. Photographed by E. Muybridge. Edited by L. S. Brown, American Museum of Natural History. 74-page introduction on mechanics of motion. 340 pages of plates, 3919 photographs. 416pp. Deluxe binding, paper. (Weight 4½ lbs.) 7⅞ x 10⅝.
T203 Clothbound **$10.00**

THE HUMAN FIGURE IN MOTION, Eadweard Muybridge. This new edition of a great classic in the history of science and photography is the largest selection ever made from the original Muybridge photos of human action: 4789 photographs, illustrating 163 types of motion: walking, running, lifting, etc. in time-exposure sequence photos at speeds up to 1/6000th of a second. Men, women, children, mostly undraped, showing bone and muscle positions against ruled backgrounds, mostly taken at 3 angles at once. Not only was this a great work of photography, acclaimed by contemporary critics as a work of genius, it was also a great 19th century landmark in biological research. Historical introduction by Prof. Robert Taft, U. of Kansas. Plates original size, full detail. Over 500 action strips. 407pp. 7¾ x 10⅝.
T204 Clothbound **$10.00**

ON THE SENSATIONS OF TONE, Hermann Helmholtz. This is an unmatched coordination of such fields as acoustical physics, physiology, experiment, history of music. It covers the entire gamut of musical tone. Partial contents: relation of vibration, resonance, analysis of tones by sympathetic resonance, beats, chords, tonality, consonant chords, discords, progression of parts, etc. 33 appendixes discuss various aspects of sound, physics, acoustics, music, etc. Translated by A. J. Ellis. New introduction by Prof. Henry Margenau of Yale. 68 figures. 43 musical passages analyzed. Over 100 tables. Index. xix + 576pp. 6⅛ x 9¼.
S114 Clothbound **$4.95**

COLLECTED WORKS OF BERNHARD RIEMANN. This important source book is the first to contain the complete text of both 1892 Werke and the 1902 supplement, unabridged. It contains 31 monographs, 3 complete lecture courses, 15 miscellaneous papers, which have been of enormous importance in relativity, topology, theory of complex variables, and other areas of mathematics. Edited by R. Dedekind, H. Weber, M. Noether, W. Wirtinger. German text. English introduction by Hans Lewy. 690pp. 5⅜ x 8.
S226 Paperbound **$2.85**

CONTRIBUTIONS TO THE FOUNDING OF THE THEORY OF TRANSFINITE NUMBERS, Georg Cantor. These papers founded a new branch of mathematics. The famous articles of 1895-7 are translated with an 82-page introduction by P. E. B. Jourdain dealing with Cantor, the background of his discoveries, their results, future possibilities. Bibliography. Index. Notes. ix + 211pp. 5⅜ x 8.
S45 Paperbound **$1.25**

PRINCIPLES OF PSYCHOLOGY, William James. This is the complete "Long Course," which is not to be confused with abridged editions. It contains all the wonderful descriptions, deep insights that have caused it to be a permanent work in all psychological libraries. Partial contents: functions of the brain, automation theories, mind-stuff theories, relation of mind to other things, consciousness, times, space, thing perception, will, emotions, hypnotism, and dozens of other areas in descriptive psychology. "A permanent classic like Locke's ESSAYS, Hume's TREATISE," John Dewey. "The preeminence of James in American psychology is unquestioned," PERSONALIST. "The American classic in psychology—unequaled in breadth and scope in the entire psychological literature," PSYCHOANALYTICAL QUARTERLY. Index. 94 figures. 2 volumes bound as one. Total of 1408pp.
T381 Vol. 1. Paperbound **$2.00**
T382 Vol. 2. Paperbound **$2.00**

RECREATIONS

SEVEN SCIENCE FICTION NOVELS OF H. G. WELLS. This is the complete text, unabridged, of seven of Wells's greatest novels: War of the Worlds, The Invisible Man, The Island of Dr. Moreau, The Food of the Gods, The First Men in the Moon, In the Days of the Comet, The Time Machine. Still considered by many experts to be the best science-fiction ever written, they will offer amusement and instruction to the scientific-minded reader. 1015pp. 5⅜ x 8.
T264 Clothbound **$3.95**

28 SCIENCE FICTION STORIES OF H. G. WELLS. Unabridged! This enormous omnibus contains 2 full-length novels—Men Like Gods, Star Begotten—plus 26 short stories of space, time, invention, biology, etc. The Crystal Egg, The Country of the Blind, Empire of the Ants, The Man Who Could Work Miracles, Aepyornis Island, A Story of the Days to Come, and 22 others! 915pp. 5⅜ x 8.   T265 Clothbound **$3.95**

FLATLAND, E. A. Abbott. This is a perennially popular science-fiction classic about life in a two-dimensioned world, and the impingement of higher dimensions. Political, satiric, humorous, moral overtones. Relativity, the fourth dimension, and other aspects of modern science are explained more clearly than in most texts. 7th edition. New introduction by Banesh Hoffmann. 128pp. 5⅜ x 8.   T1 Paperbound **$1.00**

CRYPTANALYSIS, Helen F. Gaines. (Formerly ELEMENTARY CRYPTANALYSIS.) A standard elementary and intermediate text for serious students. It does not confine itself to old material, but contains much that is not generally known except to experts. Concealment, Transposition, Substitution ciphers; Vigenere, Kasiski, Playfair, multafid, dozens of other techniques. Appendix with sequence charts, letter frequencies in English, 5 other languages, English word frequencies. Bibliography. 167 codes. New to this edition: solutions to codes. vi + 230pp. 5⅜ x 8⅜.
T97 Paperbound **$1.95**

FADS AND FALLACIES IN THE NAME OF SCIENCE, Martin Gardner. Examines various cults, quack systems, frauds, delusions which at various times have masqueraded as science. Accounts of hollow-earth fanatics like Symmes; Velikovsky and wandering planets; Hoerbiger; Bellamy and the theory of multiple moons; Charles Fort, dowsing, pseudoscientific methods for finding water, ores, oil. Sections on naturopathy, iridiagnosis, zone therapy, food fads, etc. Analytical accounts of Wilhelm Reich and orgone sex energy; L. Ron Hubbard and Dianetics; A. Korzybski and General Semantics; many others. Brought up to date to include Bridey Murphy, others. Not just a collection of anecdotes, but a fair, reasoned appraisal of eccentric theory. Formerly titled IN THE NAME OF SCIENCE. Preface. Index. x + 384pp. 5⅜ x 8.
T394 Paperbound **$1.50**

REINFELD ON THE END GAME IN CHESS, Fred Reinfeld. Analyzes 62 end games by Alekhine, Flohr, Tarrasch, Morphy, Bogolyubov, Capablanca, Vidmar, Rubinstein, Lasker, Reshevsky, other masters. Only first-rate book with extensive coverage of error; of immense aid in pointing out errors you might have made. Centers around transitions from middle play to various types of end play. King & pawn endings, minor piece endings, queen endings, bad bishops, blockage, weak pawns, passed pawns, etc. Formerly titled PRACTICAL END PLAY. 62 figures. vi + 177pp. 5⅜ x 8.   T417 Paperbound **$1.25**

PUZZLE QUIZ AND STUNT FUN, Jerome Meyer. 238 high-priority puzzles, stunts, and tricks—mathematical puzzles like The Clever Carpenter, Atom Bomb, Please Help Alice; mysteries and deductions like The Bridge of Sighs, Dog Logic, Secret Code; observation puzzlers like The American Flag, Playing Cards, Telephone Dial; more than 200 others involving magic squares, tongue twisters, puns, anagrams, word design. Answers included. Revised, enlarged edition of FUN-TO-DO. Over 100 illustrations. 238 puzzles, stunts, tricks. 256pp. 5⅜ x 8.
T337 Paperbound **$1.00**

THE BOOK OF MODERN PUZZLES, G. L. Kaufman. More than 150 word puzzles, logic puzzles. No warmed-over fare but all new material based on same appeals that make crosswords and deduction puzzles popular, but with different principles, techniques. Two-minute teasers, involved word-labyrinths, design and pattern puzzles, puzzles calling for logic and observation, puzzles testing ability to apply general knowledge to peculiar situations, many others. Answers to all problems. 116 illustrations. 192pp. 5⅜ x 8.   T143 Paperbound **$1.00**

101 PUZZLES IN THOUGHT AND LOGIC by C. R. Wylie, Jr. Designed for readers who enjoy the challenge and stimulation of logical puzzles without specialized mathematical or scientific knowledge. These problems are entirely new and range from relatively easy, to brainteasers that will afford hours of subtle entertainment. Detective problems, how to find the lying fisherman, how a blindman can identify color by logic, and many more. Easy-to-understand introduction to the logic of puzzle solving and general scientific method. 128pp. 5⅜ x 8.
T367 Paperbound **$1.00**

MATHEMAGIC, MAGIC PUZZLES, AND GAMES WITH NUMBERS, Royal V. Heath. Over 60 new puzzles and stunts based on properties of numbers. Demonstrates easy techniques for multiplying large numbers mentally, identifying unknown numbers, determining date of any day in any year, dozens of similar useful, entertaining applications of mathematics. Entertainments like The Lost Digit, 3 Acrobats, Psychic Bridge, magic squares, triangles, cubes, circles, other material not easily found elsewhere. Edited by J. S. Meyer. 76 illustrations. 128pp. 5⅜ x 8.
T110 Paperbound **$1.00**

LEARN CHESS FROM THE MASTERS, Fred Reinfeld. Improve your chess, rate your improvement, by playing against Marshall, Znosko-Borovsky, Bronstein, Najdorf, others. Formerly titled CHESS BY YOURSELF, this book contains 10 games in which you move against masters, and grade your moves by an easy system. Games selected for interest, clarity, easy principles; illustrate common openings, both classical and modern. Ratings for 114 extra playing situations that might have arisen. Full annotations. 91 diagrams. viii + 144pp. 5¾ x 8.
T362 Paperbound **$1.00**

THE COMPLETE NONSENSE OF EDWARD LEAR. Original text & illustrations of all Lear's nonsense books: A BOOK OF NONSENSE, NONSENSE SONGS, MORE NONSENSE SONGS, LAUGHABLE LYRICS, NONSENSE SONGS AND STORIES. Only complete edition available at popular price. Old favorites such as The Dong With a Luminous Nose, hundreds of other delightful bits of nonsense for children & adults. 214 different limericks, each illustrated by Lear; 3 different sets of Nonsense Botany; 5 Nonsense Alphabets; many others. 546 illustrations. 320pp. 5⅜ x 8.
T167 Paperbound **$1.00**

CRYPTOGRAPHY, D. Smith. Excellent elementary introduction to enciphering, deciphering secret writing. Explains transposition, substitution ciphers; codes; solutions. Geometrical patterns, route transcription, columnar transposition, other methods. Mixed cipher systems; single-alphabet, polyalphabetical substitution; mechanical devices; Vigenere system, etc. Enciphering Japanese; explanation of Baconian Biliteral cipher frequency tables. More than 150 problems provide practical application. Bibliography. Index. 164pp. 5⅜ x 8.
T247 Paperbound **$1.00**

MATHEMATICAL EXCURSIONS, Helen A. Merrill. Fun, recreation, insights into elementary problem-solving. A mathematical expert guides you along by-paths not generally travelled in elementary math courses—how to divide by inspection, Russian peasant system of multiplication; memory systems for pi; building odd and even magic squares; dyadic systems; facts about 37; square roots by geometry; Tchebichev's machine; drawing five-sided figures; dozens more. Solutions to more difficult ones. 50 illustrations. 145pp. 5⅜ x 8.
T350 Paperbound **$1.00**

MATHEMATICAL RECREATIONS, M. Kraitchik. Some 250 puzzles, problems, demonstrations of recreational mathematics for beginners & advanced mathematicians. Unusual historical problems from Greek, Medieval, Arabic, Hindu sources; modern problems based on "mathematics without numbers," geometry, topology, arithmetic, etc. Pastimes derived from figurative numbers, Mersenne numbers, Fermat numbers; fairy chess; latruncles; reversi, many other topics. Full solutions. Excellent for insights into special fields of math. 181 illustrations. 330pp. 5⅜ x 8.
T163 Paperbound **$1.75**

MATHEMATICAL PUZZLES FOR BEGINNERS AND ENTHUSIASTS, G. Mott-Smith. 188 mathematical puzzles to test mental agility. Inference, interpretation, algebra, dissection of plane figures, geometry, properties of numbers, decimation, permutations, probability, all enter these delightful problems. Puzzles like the Odic Force, How to Draw an Ellipse, Spider's Cousin, more than 180 others. Detailed solutions. Appendix with square roots, triangular numbers, primes, etc. 135 illustrations. 2nd revised edition. 248pp. 5⅜ x 8.
T198 Paperbound **$1.00**

NEW WORD PUZZLES, Gerald L. Kaufman. Contains 100 brand new challenging puzzles based on words and their combinations, never published before in any form. Most are new types invented by the author—for beginners or experts. Chess word puzzles, addle letter anagrams, double word squares, double horizontals, alphagram puzzles, dual acrostigrams, linkogram lapwords—plus 8 other brand new types, all with solutions included. 196 figures. 100 brand new puzzles. vi + 122pp. 5⅜ x 8.
T344 Paperbound **$1.00**

MATHEMATICS, MAGIC AND MYSTERY, Martin Gardner. Card tricks, feats of mental mathematics, stage mind-reading, other "magic" explained as applications of probability, sets, theory of numbers, topology, various branches of mathematics. Creative examination of laws and their application, with sources of new tricks and insights. 115 sections discuss tricks with cards, dice, coins; geometrical vanishing tricks, dozens of others. No sleight of hand needed; mathematics guarantees success. 115 illustrations. xii + 174pp. 5⅜ x 8.
T335 Paperbound **$1.00**

MATHEMATICS ELEMENTARY TO INTERMEDIATE

HOW TO CALCULATE QUICKLY, Henry Sticker. This handy volume offers a tried and true method for helping you in the basic mathematics of daily life—addition, subtraction, multiplication, division, fractions, etc. It is designed to awaken your "number sense" or the ability to see relationships between numbers as whole quantities. It is not a collection of tricks working only on special numbers, but a serious course of over 9,000 problems and their solutions, teaching special techniques not taught in schools: left-to-right multiplication, new fast ways of division, etc. 5 or 10 minutes daily use will double or triple your calculation speed. Excellent for the scientific worker who is at home in higher math, but is not satisfied with his speed and accuracy in lower mathematics. 256pp. 5 x 7¼.
T295 Paperbound **$1.00**

FAMOUS PROBLEMS OF ELEMENTARY GEOMETRY, Felix Klein. Expanded version of the 1894 Easter lectures at Göttingen. 3 problems of classical geometry: squaring circle, trisecting angle, doubling cube, considered with full modern implications: transcendental numbers, pi, etc. Notes by R. Archibald. 16 figures. xi + 92pp. 5⅜ x 8.
T348 Clothbound **$1.50**
T298 Paperbound **$1.00**

HIGHER MATHEMATICS FOR STUDENTS OF CHEMISTRY AND PHYSICS, J. W. Mellor. Not abstract, but practical, building its problems out of familiar laboratory material, this covers differential calculus, coordinate, analytical geometry, functions, integral calculus, infinite series, numerical equations, differential equations, Fourier's theorem, probability, theory of errors, calculus of variations, determinants. "If the reader is not familiar with this book, it will repay him to examine it," CHEM. & ENGINEERING NEWS. 800 problems, 189 figures. Bibliography. xxi + 641pp. 5⅜ x 8.
S193 Paperbound **$2.00**

TRIGONOMETRY REFRESHER FOR TECHNICAL MEN, A. Albert Klaf. 913 detailed questions and answers cover the most important aspects of plane and spherical trigonometry. They will help you to brush up or to clear up difficulties in special areas.—The first portion of this book covers plane trigonometry, including angles, quadrants, trigonometrical functions, graphical representation, interpolation, equations, logarithms, solution of triangle, use of the slide rule and similar topics–188 pages then discuss application of plane trigonometry to special problems in navigation, surveying, elasticity, architecture, and various fields of engineering. Small angles, periodic functions, vectors, polar coordinates, De Moivre's theorem are fully examined—The third section of the book then' discusses spherical trigonometry and the solution of spherical triangles, with their applications to terrestrial and astronomical problems. Methods of saving time with numerical calculations, simplification of principal functions of angle, much practical information make this a most useful book—913 questions answered. 1738 problems, answers to odd numbers. 494 figures. 24 pages of useful formulae, functions. Index. x + 629pp. 5⅜ x 8.
T371 Paperbound **$2.00**

CALCULUS REFRESHER FOR TECHNICAL MEN, A. Albert Klaf. This book is unique in English as a refresher for engineers, technicians, students who either wish to brush up their calculus or to clear up uncertainties. It is not an ordinary text, but an examination of most important aspects of integral and differential calculus in terms of the 756 questions most likely to occur to the technical reader. The first part of this book covers simple differential calculus, with constants, variables, functions, increments, derivatives, differentiation, logarithms, curvature of curves, and similar topics—The second part covers fundamental ideas of integration, inspection, substitution, transformation, reduction, areas and volumes, mean value, successive and partial integration, double and triple integration. Practical aspects are stressed rather than theoretical. A 50-page section illustrates the application of calculus to specific problems of civil and nautical engineering, electricity, stress and strain, elasticity, industrial engineering, and similar fields.— 756 questions answered. 566 problems, mostly answered. 36 pages of useful constants, formulae for ready reference. Index. v + 431pp. 5⅜ x 8. T370 Paperbound **$2.00**

MONOGRAPHS ON TOPICS OF MODERN MATHEMATICS, edited by **J. W. A. Young.** Advanced mathematics for persons who haven't gone beyond or have forgotten high school algebra. 9 monographs on foundation of geometry, modern pure geometry, non-Euclidean geometry, fundamental propositions of algebra, algebraic equations, functions, calculus, theory of numbers, etc. Each monograph gives proofs of important results, and descriptions of leading methods, to provide wide coverage. New introduction by Prof. M. Kline, N. Y. University. 100 diagrams. xvi + 416pp. 6⅛ x 9¼. S289 Paperbound **$2.00**

MATHEMATICS: INTERMEDIATE TO ADVANCED

INTRODUCTION TO THE THEORY OF FOURIER'S SERIES AND INTEGRALS, H. S. Carslaw. 3rd revised edition. This excellent introduction is an outgrowth of the author's courses at Cambridge. Historical introduction, rational and irrational numbers, infinite sequences and series, functions of a single variable, definite integral, Fourier series, Fourier integrals, and similar topics. Appendixes discuss practical harmonic analysis, periodogram analysis, Lebesgues theory. Indexes. 84 examples, bibliography. xiii + 368 pp. 5⅜ x 8. S48 Paperbound **$2.00**

INTRODUCTION TO THE THEORY OF NUMBERS, L. E. Dickson. Thorough, comprehensive approach with adequate coverage of classical literature, an introductory volume beginners can follow. Chapters on divisibility, congruences, quadratic residues & reciprocity, Diophantine equations, etc. Full treatment of binary quadratic forms without usual restriction to integral coefficients. Covers infinitude of primes, least residues, Fermat's theorem, Euler's phi function, Legendre's symbol, Gauss's lemma, automorphs, reduced forms, recent theorems of Thue & Siegel, many more. Much material not readily available elsewhere. 239 problems. Index. 1 figure. viii + 183pp. 5⅜ x 8. S342 Paperbound **$1.65**

MECHANICS VIA THE CALCULUS, P. W. Norris, W. S. Legge. Covers almost everything from linear motion to vector analysis: equations determining motion, linear methods, compounding of simple harmonic motions, Newton's laws of motion, Hooke's law, the simple pendulum, motion of a particle in 1 plane, centers of gravity, virtual work, friction, kinetic energy of rotating bodies, equilibrium of strings, hydrostatics, sheering stresses, elasticity, etc. 550 problems. 3rd revised edition. xii + 367pp. S207 Clothbound **$3.95**

NON-EUCLIDEAN GEOMETRY, Roberto Bonola. The standard coverage of non-Euclidean geometry. It examines from both a historical and mathematical point of view the geometries which have arisen from a study of Euclid's 5th postulate upon parallel lines. Also included are complete texts, translated, of Bolyai's THEORY OF ABSOLUTE SPACE, Lobachevsky's THEORY OF PARALLELS. 180 diagrams. 431pp. 5⅜ x 8. S27 Paperbound **$1.95**

ELEMENTS OF THE THEORY OF REAL FUNCTIONS, J. E. Littlewood. Based on lectures given at Trinity College, Cambridge, this book has proved to be extremely successful in introducing graduate students to the modern theory of functions. It offers a full and concise coverage of classes and cardinal numbers, well-ordered series, other types of series, and elements of the theory of sets of points. 3rd revised edition. vii + 71pp. 5⅜ x 8. S171 Clothbound **$2.85**
S172 Paperbound **$1.25**

THE CONTINUUM AND OTHER TYPES OF SERIAL ORDER, E. V. Huntington. This famous book gives a systematic elementary account of the modern history of the continuum as a type of serial order. Based on the Cantor-Dedekind ordinal theory, which requires no technical knowledge of higher mathematics, it offers an easily followed analysis of ordered classes, discrete and dense series, continuous series, Cantor's transfinite numbers. 2nd edition. Index. viii + 82pp. 5⅜ x 8.
S129 Clothbound **$2.75**
S130 Paperbound **$1.00**

GEOMETRY OF FOUR DIMENSIONS, H. P. Manning. Unique in English as a clear, concise introduction. Treatment is synthetic, and mostly Euclidean, although in hyperplanes and hyperspheres at infinity, non-Euclidean geometry is used. Historical introduction. Foundations of 4-dimensional geometry. Perpendicularity, simple angles. Angles of planes, higher order. Symmetry, order, motion; hyperpyramids, hypercones, hyperspheres; figures with parallel elements; volume, hypervolume in space; regular polyhedroids. Glossary. 78 figures. ix + 348pp. 5⅜ x 8.
S181 Clothbound **$3.95**
S182 Paperbound **$1.95**

VECTOR AND TENSOR ANALYSIS, G. E. Hay. One of the clearest introductions to this increasingly important subject. Start with simple definitions, finish the book with a sure mastery of oriented Cartesian vectors, Christoffel symbols, solenoidal tensors, and their applications. Complete breakdown of plane, solid, analytical, differential geometry. Separate chapters on application. All fundamental formulae listed & demonstrated. 195 problems, 66 figures. viii + 193pp. 5⅜ x 8.
S109 Paperbound **$1.75**

INTRODUCTION TO THE DIFFERENTIAL EQUATIONS OF PHYSICS, L. Hopf. Especially valuable to the engineer with no math beyond elementary calculus. Emphasizing intuitive rather than formal aspects of concepts, the author covers an extensive territory. Partial contents: Law of causality, energy theorem, damped oscillations, coupling by friction, cylindrical and spherical coordinates, heat source, etc. Index. 48 figures. 160pp. 5⅜ x 8. S120 Paperbound **$1.25**

INTRODUCTION TO THE THEORY OF GROUPS OF FINITE ORDER, R. Carmichael. Examines fundamental theorems and their application. Beginning with sets, systems, permutations, etc., it progresses in easy stages through important types of groups: Abelian, prime power, permutation, etc. Except 1 chapter where matrices are desirable, no higher math needed. 783 exercises, problems. Index. xvi + 447pp. 5⅜ x 8.
S299 Clothbound **$3.95**
S300 Paperbound **$2.00**

THEORY OF GROUPS OF FINITE ORDER, W. Burnside. First published some 40 years ago, this is still one of the clearest introductory texts. Partial contents: permutations, groups independent of representation, composition series of a group, isomorphism of a group with itself, Abelian groups, prime power groups, permutation groups, invariants of groups of linear substitution, graphical representation, etc. 45pp. of notes. Indexes. xxiv + 512pp. 5⅜ x 8.
S38 Paperbound **$2.45**

INFINITE SEQUENCES AND SERIES, Konrad Knopp. First publication in any language! Excellent introduction to 2 topics of modern mathematics, designed to give the student background to penetrate farther by himself. Sequences & sets, real & complex numbers, etc. Functions of a real & complex variable. Sequences & series. Infinite series. Convergent power series. Expansion of elementary functions. Numerical evaluation of series. Bibliography. v + 186pp. 5⅜ x 8.
S152 Clothbound **$3.50**
S153 Paperbound **$1.75**

THEORY OF SETS, E. Kamke. Clearest, amplest introduction in English, well suited for independent study. Subdivisions of main theory, such as theory of sets of points, are discussed, but emphasis is on general theory. Partial contents: rudiments of set theory, arbitrary sets and their cardinal numbers, ordered sets and their order types, well-ordered sets and their ordinal numbers. Bibliography. Key to symbols. Index. vii + 144pp. 5⅜ x 8. S141 Paperbound **$1.35**

ELEMENTS OF NUMBER THEORY, I. M. Vinogradov. Detailed 1st course for persons without advanced mathematics; 95% of this book can be understood by readers who have gone no farther than high school algebra. Partial contents: divisibility theory, important number theoretical functions, congruences, primitive roots and indices, etc. Solutions to both problems and exercises. Tables of primes, indices, etc. Covers almost every essential formula in elementary number theory! 233 problems, 104 exercises. viii + 227pp. 5⅜ x 8. S259 Paperbound **$1.60**

FIVE VOLUME "THEORY OF FUNCTIONS" SET BY KONRAD KNOPP. This five-volume set, prepared by Konrad Knopp, provides a complete and readily followed account of theory of functions. Proofs are given concisely, yet without sacrifice of completeness or rigor. These volumes are used as texts by such universities as M.I.T., University of Chicago, N. Y. City College, and many others. "Excellent introduction . . . remarkably readable, concise, clear, rigorous," JOURNAL OF THE AMERICAN STATISTICAL ASSOCIATION.

ELEMENTS OF THE THEORY OF FUNCTIONS, Konrad Knopp. This book provides the student with background for further volumes in this set, or texts on a similar level. Partial contents: Foundations, system of complex numbers and the Gaussian plane of numbers, Riemann sphere of numbers, mapping by linear functions, normal forms, the logarithm, the cyclometric functions and binomial series. "Not only for the young student, but also for the student who knows all about what is in it," MATHEMATICAL JOURNAL. Bibliography. Index. 140pp. 5⅜ x 8. S154 Paperbound **$1.35**

THEORY OF FUNCTIONS, PART I., Konrad Knopp. With volume II, this book provides coverage of basic concepts and theorems. Partial contents: numbers and points, functions of a complex variable, integral of a continuous function, Cauchy's integral theorem, Cauchy's integral formulae, series with variable terms, expansion of analytic functions in power series, analytic continuation and complete definition of analytic functions, entire transcendental functions, Laurent expansion, types of singularities. Bibliography. Index. vii + 146pp. 5⅜ x 8.   S156 Paperbound **$1.35**

THEORY OF FUNCTIONS, PART II., Konrad Knopp. Application and further development of general theory, special topics. Single valued functions: entire, Weierstrass. Meromorphic functions: Mittag-Leffler. Periodic functions. Multiple-valued functions. Riemann surfaces. Algebraic functions. Analytical configuration, Riemann surface. Bibliography. Index. x + 150pp. 5⅜ x 8.
S157 Paperbound **$1.35**

PROBLEM BOOK IN THE THEORY OF FUNCTIONS, VOLUME 1., Konrad Knopp. Problems in elementary theory, for use with Knopp's THEORY OF FUNCTIONS, or any other text, arranged according to increasing difficulty. Fundamental concepts, sequences of numbers and infinite series, complex variable, integral theorem, development in series, conformal mapping. Answers. viii + 126pp. 5⅜ x 8.   S158 Paperbound **$1.35**

PROBLEM BOOK IN THE THEORY OF FUNCTIONS, VOLUME 2, Konrad Knopp. Advanced theory of functions, to be used either with Knopp's THEORY OF FUNCTIONS, or any other comparable text. Singularities, entire & meromorphic functions, periodic, analytic, continuation, multiple-valued functions, Riemann surfaces, conformal mapping. Includes a section of additional elementary problems. "The difficult task of selecting from the immense material of the modern theory of functions the problems just within the reach of the beginner is here masterfully accomplished," AM. MATH. SOC. Answers. 138pp. 5⅜ x 8.   S159 Paperbound **$1.35**

SYMBOLIC LOGIC

AN INTRODUCTION TO SYMBOLIC LOGIC, Susanne K. Langer. Probably the clearest book ever written on symbolic logic for the philosopher, general scientist and layman. It will be particularly appreciated by those who have been rebuffed by other introductory works because of insufficient mathematical training. No special knowledge of mathematics is required. Starting with the simplest symbols and conventions, you are led to a remarkable grasp of the Boole-Schroeder and Russell-Whitehead systems clearly and quickly. PARTIAL CONTENTS: Study of forms, Essentials of logical structure, Generalization, Classes, The deductive system of classes, The algebra of logic, Abstraction of interpretation, Calculus of propositions, Assumptions of PRINCIPIA MATHEMATICA, Logistics, Logic of the syllogism, Proofs of theorems. "One of the clearest and simplest introductions to a subject which is very much alive. The style is easy, symbolism is introduced gradually, and the intelligent non-mathematican should have no difficulty in following argument," MATHEMATICS GAZETTE. Revised, expanded second edition. Truth-value tables. 368pp. 5⅜ x 8.
S164 Paperbound **$1.75**

THE ELEMENTS OF MATHEMATICAL LOGIC, Paul Rosenbloom. FIRST PUBLICATION IN ANY LANGUAGE. This book is intended for readers who are mature mathematically, but have no previous training in symbolic logic. It does not limit itself to a single system, but covers the field as a whole. It is a development of lectures given at Lund University, Sweden in 1948. Partial contents: Logic of classes, fundamental theorems, Boolean algebra, logic of propositions, logic of propositional functions, expressive languages, combinatory logics, development of mathematics within an object language, paradoxes, theorems of Post and Goedel, Church's theorem, and similar topics. iv + 214pp. 5⅜ x 8.   S277 Paperbound **$1.45**

THE LAWS OF THOUGHT, George Boole. This book founded symbolic logic some hundred years ago. It is the 1st significant attempt to apply logic to all aspects of human endeavour. Partial contents: derivation of laws, signs & laws, interpretations, eliminations, conditions of a perfect method, analysis, Aristotelian logic, probability, and similar topics. xviii + 424pp. 5⅜ x 8.
S28 Paperbound **$2.00**

ELEMENTARY MATHEMATICS FROM AN ADVANCED STANDPOINT, Felix Klein.

This classic text is an outgrowth of Klein's famous integration and survey course at Göttingen. Using one field of mathematics to interpret, adjust, illuminate another, it covers basic topics in each area, illustrating its discussion with extensive analysis. It is especially valuable in considering areas of modern mathematics. "Makes the reader feel the inspiration of . . . a great mathematician, inspiring teacher . . . with deep insight into the foundations and interrelations," BULLETIN, AMERICAN MATHEMATICAL SOCIETY.

Vol. 1. ARITHMETIC, ALGEBRA, ANALYSIS. Introducing the concept of function immediately, it enlivens abstract discussion with graphical and geometrically perceptual methods. Partial contents: natural numbers, extension of the notion of number, special properties, complex numbers. Real equations with real unknowns, complex quantities. Logarithmic, exponential functions, goniometric functions, infinitesimal calculus. Transcendence of e and pi, theory of assemblages. Index. 125 figures. ix + 247pp. 5⅜ x 8.   S150 Paperbound **$1.75**

Vol. 2. GEOMETRY. A comprehensive view which accompanies the space perception inherent in geometry with analytic formulas which facilitate precise formulation. Partial contents: Simplest geometric manifolds: line segment, Grassmann determinant principles, classification of configurations of space, derivative manifolds. Geometric transformations: affine transformations, projective, higher point transformations, theory of the imaginary. Systematic discussion of geometry and its foundations. Indexes. 141 illustrations. ix + 214pp. 5⅜ x 8.   S151 Paperbound **$1.75**

MATHEMATICS: ADVANCED

ALMOST PERIODIC FUNCTIONS, A. S. Besicovitch. This unique and important summary by a well-known mathematician covers in detail the two stages of development in Bohr's theory of almost periodic functions: (1) as a generalization of pure periodicity, with results and proofs; (2) the work done by Stepanoff, Wiener, Weyl, and Bohr in generalizing the theory. Bibliography. xi + 180pp. 5⅜ x 8.   S17 Clothbound **$3.50**
S18 Paperbound **$1.75**

LECTURES ON THE ICOSAHEDRON AND THE SOLUTION OF EQUATIONS OF THE FIFTH DEGREE, Felix Klein. The solution of quintics in terms of rotations of a regular icosahedron around its axes of symmetry. A classic & indispensable source for those interested in higher algebra, geometry, crystallography. Considerable explanatory material included. 230 footnotes, mostly bibliographic. 2nd edition, xvi + 289pp. 5⅜ x 8.   S314 Paperbound **$1.85**

LINEAR INTEGRAL EQUATIONS, W. V. Lovitt. Systematic survey of general theory, with some application to differential equations, calculus of variations problems of math, physics. Partial contents: integral equations of 2nd kind by successive substitutions; Fredholm's equation as ratio of 2 integral series in lambda, applications of the Fredholm theory, Hilbert-Schmidt theory of symmetric kernels, application, etc. Neumann, Dirichlet, vibratory problems. Index. ix + 253pp. 5⅜ x 8.   S175 Clothbound **$3.50**
S176 Paperbound **$1.60**

MATHEMATICAL FOUNDATIONS OF STATISTICAL MECHANICS, A. I. Khinchin. Offering a precise and rigorous formulation of problems, this book supplies a thorough and up-to-date exposition. It provides analytical tools needed to replace cumbersome concepts, and furnishes for the first time a logical step-by-step introduction to the subject. Partial contents: geometry & kinematics of the phase space, ergodic problem, reduction to theory of probability, application of central limit problem, ideal monatomic gas, foundation of thermodynamics, dispersion and distributions of sum functions. Key to notations. Index. xiii + 179pp. 5⅜ x 8.   S146 Clothbound **$2.95**
S147 Paperbound **$1.35**

ORDINARY DIFFERENTIAL EQUATIONS, E. L. Ince. A most compendious analysis in real and complex domains. Existence and nature of solutions, continuous transformation groups, solutions in an infinite form, definite integrals, algebraic theory, Sturmian theory, boundary problems, existence theorems, 1st order, higher order, etc. "Deserves the highest praise, a notable addition to mathematical literature," BULLETIN, AM. MATH. SOC. Historical appendix. Bibliography. 18 figures. viii + 558pp. 5⅜ x 8.   S349 Paperbound **$2.55**

TRIGONOMETRICAL SERIES, Antoni Zygmund. Unique in any language on modern advanced level. Contains carefully organized analyses of trigonometric, orthogonal, Fourier systems of functions, with clear adequate descriptions of summability of Fourier series, proximation theory, conjugate series, convergence, divergence of Fourier series. Especially valuable for Russian, Eastern European coverage. Bibliography. 329pp. 5⅜ x 8.   S290 Paperbound **$1.50**

FOUNDATIONS OF POTENTIAL THEORY, O. D. Kellogg. Based on courses given at Harvard this is suitable for both advanced and beginning mathematicians. Proofs are rigorous, and much material not generally available elsewhere is included. Partial contents: forces of gravity, fields of force, divergence theorem, properties of Newtonian potentials at points of free space, potentials as solutions of Laplace's equations, harmonic functions, electrostatics, electric images, logarithmic potential, etc. ix + 384pp. 5⅜ x 8.   S144 Paperbound **$1.98**

LECTURES ON CAUCHY'S PROBLEMS, J. Hadamard. Based on lectures given at Columbia and Rome, this discusses work of Riemann, Kirchhoff, Volterra, and the author's own research on the hyperbolic case in linear partial differential equations. It extends spherical and cylindrical waves to apply to all (normal) hyperbolic equations. Partial contents: Cauchy's problem, fundamental formula, equations with odd number, with even number of independent variables; method of descent. 32 figures. Index. iii + 361pp. 5⅜ x 8.   S105 Paperbound **$1.75**

MATHEMATICAL PHYSICS, STATISTICS

THE MATHEMATICAL THEORY OF ELASTICITY, A. E. H. Love. A wealth of practical illustration combined with thorough discussion of fundamentals—theory, application, special problems and solutions. Partial contents: Analysis of Strain & Stress, Elasticity of Solid Bodies, Isotropic Elastic Solids, Equilibrium of Aeolotropic Elastic Solids, Elasticity of Crystals, Vibration of Spheres, Cylinders, Propagation of Waves in Elastic Solid Media, Torsion, Theory of Continuous Beams, Plates. Rigorous treatment of Volterra's theory of dislocations, 2-dimensional elastic systems, other topics of modern interest. "For years the standard treatise on elasticity," AMERICAN MATHEMATICAL MONTHLY. 4th revised edition. Index. 76 figures. xviii + 643pp. 6⅛ x 9¼.   S174 Paperbound **$2.95**

TABLES OF FUNCTIONS WITH FORMULAE AND CURVES, E. Jahnke & F. Emde. The world's most comprehensive 1-volume English-text collection of tables, formulae, curves of transcendent functions. 4th corrected edition, new 76-page section giving tables, formulae for elementary functions—not in other English editions. Partial contents: sine, cosine, logarithmic integral; factorial function; error integral; theta functions; elliptic integrals, functions; Legendre, Bessel, Riemann, Mathieu, hypergeometric functions, etc. Supplementary books. Bibliography. Indexed. "Out of the way functions for which we know no other source," SCIENTIFIC COMPUTING SERVICE, Ltd. 212 figures. 400pp. 5⅜ x 8.   S133 Paperbound **$2.00**

PRACTICAL ANALYSIS, GRAPHICAL AND NUMERICAL METHODS, F. A. Willers. Translated by R. T. Beyer. Immensely practical handbook for engineers, showing how to interpolate, use various methods of numerical differentiation and integration, determine the roots of a single algebraic equation, system of linear equations, use empirical formulas, integrate differential equations, etc. Hundreds of shortcuts for arriving at numerical solutions. Special section on American calculating machines, by T. W. Simpson. 132 illustrations. 422pp. 5⅜ x 8. S273 Paperbound **$2.00**

DICTIONARY OF CONFORMAL REPRESENTATIONS, H. Kober. Laplace's equation in 2 dimensions solved in this unique book developed by the British Admiralty. Scores of geometrical forms & their transformations for electrical engineers, Joukowski aerofoil for aerodynamists, Schwartz-Christoffel transformations for hydrodynamics, transcendental functions. Contents classified according to analytical functions describing transformation. Twin diagrams show curves of most transformations with corresponding regions. Glossary. Topological index. 447 diagrams. 244pp. 6⅛ x 9¼. S160 Paperbound **$2.00**

FREQUENCY CURVES AND CORRELATION, W. P. Elderton. 4th revised edition of a standard work covering classical statistics. It is practical in approach, and one of the books most frequently referred to for clear presentation of basic material. Partial contents. Frequency distributions. Method of moment. Pearson's frequency curves. Correlation. Theoretical distributions, spurious correlation. Correlation of characters not quantitatively measurable. Standard errors. Test of goodness of fit. The correlation ratio—contingency. Partial correlation. Corrections for moments, beta and gamma functions, etc. Key to terms, symbols. Bibliography. 25 examples in text. 40 useful tables. 16 figures. xi + 272pp. 5½ x 8½. Clothbound **$1.49**

HYDRODYNAMICS, H. Dryden, F. Murnaghan, Harry Bateman. Published by the National Research Council in 1932 this enormous volume offers a complete coverage of classical hydrodynamics. Encyclopedic in quality. Partial contents: physics of fluids, motion, turbulent flow, compressible fluids, motion in 1, 2, 3 dimensions; viscous fluids rotating, laminar motion, resistance of motion through viscous fluid, eddy viscosity, hydraulic flow in channels of various shapes, discharge of gases, flow past obstacles, etc. Bibliography of over 2,900 items. Indexes. 23 figures. 634pp. 5⅜ x 8. S303 Paperbound **$2.75**

HYDRODYNAMICS, A STUDY OF LOGIC, FACT, AND SIMILITUDE, Garrett Birkhoff. A stimulating application of pure mathematics to an applied problem. Emphasis is placed upon correlation of theory and deduction with experiment. It examines carefully recently discovered paradoxes, theory of modelling and dimensional analysis, paradox & error in flows and free boundary theory. The author derives the classical theory of virtual mass from homogeneous spaces, and applies group theory to fluid mechanics. Index. Bibliography. 20 figures, 3 plates. xiii + 186pp. 5⅜ x 8. S21 Clothbound **$3.50**
S22 Paperbound **$1.85**

HYDRODYNAMICS, Horace Lamb. Internationally famous complete coverage of standard reference work on dynamics of liquids & gases. Fundamental theorems, equations, methods, solutions, background, for classical hydrodynamics. Chapters include Equations of Motion, Integration of Equations in Special Gases, Irrotational Motion, Motion of Liquid in 2 Dimensions, Motion of Solids through Liquid—Dynamical Theory, Vortex Motion, Tidal Waves, Surface Waves, Waves of Expansion, Viscosity, Rotating Masses of Liquids. Excellently planned, arranged; clear, lucid presentation. 6th enlarged, revised edition. Index. Over 900 footnotes, mostly bibliographical. 119 figures. xv + 738pp. 6⅛ x 9¼. S256 Paperbound **$2.95**

INTRODUCTION TO RELAXATION METHODS, F. S. Shaw. Fluid mechanics, design of electrical networks, forces in structural frameworks, stress distribution, buckling, etc. Solve linear simultaneous equations, linear ordinary differential equations, partial differential equations, Eigenvalue problems by relaxation methods. Detailed examples throughout. Special tables for dealing with awkwardly-shaped boundaries. Indexes. 253 diagrams. 72 tables. 400pp. 5⅜ x 8. S244 Paperbound **$2.45**

PARTIAL DIFFERENTIAL EQUATIONS OF MATHEMATICAL PHYSICS, A. G. Webster. A keystone work in the library of every mature physicist, engineer, researcher. Valuable sections on elasticity, compression theory, potential theory, theory of sound, heat conduction, wave propagation, vibration theory. Contents include: deduction of differential equations, vibrations, normal functions, Fourier's series, Cauchy's method, boundary problems, method of Riemann-Volterra. Spherical, cylindrical, ellipsoidal harmonics, applications, etc. 97 figures. vii + 440pp. 5⅜ x 8. S263 Paperbound **$1.98**

THE THEORY OF GROUPS AND QUANTUM MECHANICS, H. Weyl. Discussions of Schroedinger's wave equation, de Broglie's waves of a particle, Jordon-Hoelder theorem, Lie's continuous groups of transformations, Pauli exclusion principle, quantization of Maxwell-Dirac field equations, etc. symmetry permutation group, algebra of symmetric transformation, etc. 2nd revised edition. Unitary geometry, quantum theory, groups, application of groups to quantum mechanics, symmetry permutation group, algebra of symmetric transformation, etc. 2nd revised edition. Bibliography. Index. xxii + 422pp. 5⅜ x 8. S268 Clothbound **$4.50**
S269 Paperbound **$1.95**

PARTIAL DIFFERENTIAL EQUATIONS OF MATHEMATICAL PHYSICS, Harry Bateman. Solution of boundary value problems by means of definite analytical expressions, with wide range of representative problems, full reference to contemporary literature, and new material by the author. Partial contents: classical equations, integral theorems of Green, Stokes; 2-dimensional problems; conformal representation; equations in 3 variables; polar coordinates; cylindrical, ellipsoidal, paraboloid, toroidal coordinates; non-linear equations, etc. "Must be in the hands of everyone interested in boundary value problems," BULLETIN, AM. MATH. SOC. Indexes. 450 bibliographic footnotes. 175 examples. 29 illustrations. xxii + 552pp. 6 x 9. S15 Clothbound **$4.95**

NUMERICAL SOLUTIONS OF DIFFERENTIAL EQUATIONS, H. Levy & E. A. Baggott. Comprehensive collection of methods for solving ordinary differential equations of first and higher order. All must pass 2 requirements: easy to grasp and practical, more rapid than school methods. Partial contents: graphical integration of differential equations, graphical methods for detailed solution. Numerical solution. Simultaneous equations and equations of 2nd and higher orders. "Should be in the hands of all in research in applied mathematics, teaching," NATURE. 21 figures. viii + 238pp. $5\frac{3}{8}$ x 8. S168 Paperbound **$1.75**

ASYMPTOTIC EXPANSIONS, A. Erdélyi. The only modern work available in English, this is an unabridged reproduction of a monograph prepared for the Office of Naval Research. It discusses various procedures for asymptotic evaluation of integrals containing a large parameter and solutions of ordinary linear differential equations. Bibliography of 71 items. vi + 108pp. $5\frac{3}{8}$ x 8. S318 Paperbound **$1.35**

THE FOURIER INTEGRAL AND CERTAIN OF ITS APPLICATIONS, Norbert Wiener. The only book-length study of the Fourier integral as link between pure and applied math. An expansion of lectures given at Cambridge. Partial contents: Plancherel's theorem, general Tauberian theorem, special Tauberian theorms, generalized harmonic analysis. Bibliography. viii + 201pp. $5\frac{3}{8}$ x 8. S272 Clothbound **$3.95**

THE THEORY OF SOUND, Lord Rayleigh. Most vibrating systems likely to be encountered in practice can be tackled successfully by the methods set forth by the great Noble laureate, Lord Rayleigh. Complete coverage of experimental, mathematical aspects of sound theory. Partial contents: Harmonic motions, vibrating systems in general, lateral vibrations of bars, curved plates or shells, applications of Laplace's functions to acoustical problems, fluid friction, plane vortex-sheet, vibrations of solid bodies, etc. This is the first inexpensive edition of this great reference and study work. Bibliography. Historical introduction by R. B. Lindsay. Total of 1040pp. 97 figures. $5\frac{3}{8}$ x 8. S292, S293, Two volume set, paperbound **$4.00**

ANALYSIS & DESIGN OF EXPERIMENTS, H. B. Mann. Offers a method for grasping the analysis of variance and variance design within a short time. Partial contents: Chi-square distribution and analysis of variance distribution, matrices, quadratic forms, likelihood ratio tests and tests of linear hypotheses, power of analysis, Galois fields, non-orthogonal data, interblock estimates, etc. 15pp. of useful tables. x + 195pp. 5 x $7\frac{3}{8}$. S180 Paperbound **$1.45**

MATHEMATICAL ANALYSIS OF ELECTRICAL AND OPTICAL WAVE-MOTION, Harry Bateman. Written by one of this century's most distinguished mathematical physicists, this is a practical introduction to those developments of Maxwell's electromagnetic theory which are directly connected with the solution of the partial differential equation of wave motion. Methods of solving wave-equations, polar-cylindrical coordinates, diffraction, transformation of coordinates, homogeneous solutions, electromagnetic fields with moving singularities, etc. Index. 168pp. $5\frac{3}{8}$ x 8. S14 Paperbound **$1.60**

PHYSICAL PRINCIPLES OF THE QUANTUM THEORY, Werner Heisenberg. A Nobel laureate discusses quantum theory; Heisenberg's own work, Compton, Schroedinger, Wilson, Einstein, many others. Written for physicists, chemists who are not specialists in quantum theory, only elementary formulae are considered in the text; there is a mathematical appendix for specialists. Profound without sacrifice of clarity. Translated by C. Eckart, F. Hoyt. 18 figures. 192pp. $5\frac{3}{8}$ x 8. S113 Paperbound **$1.25**

FOUNDATIONS OF NUCLEAR PHYSICS, edited by R. T. Beyer. 13 of the most important papers on nuclear physics reproduced in facsimile in the original languages of their authors: the papers most often cited in footnotes, bibliographies. Anderson, Curie, Joliot, Chadwick, Fermi, Lawrence, Cockcroft, Hahn, Yukawa. Unparalleled Bibliography: 122 double-columned pages, over 4,000 articles, books, classified. 57 figures. 288pp. $6\frac{1}{8}$ x $9\frac{1}{4}$. S19 Paperbound **$1.75**

SELECTED PAPERS ON NOISE AND STOCHASTIC PROCESS, edited by Prof. Nelson Wax, U. of Illinois. 6 basic papers for newcomers in the field, for those whose work involves noise characteristics. Chandrasekhar, Uhlenbeck & Ornstein, Uhlenbeck & Ming, Rice, Doob. Included is Kac's Chauvenet-Prize winning Random Walk. Extensive bibliography lists 200 articles; up through 1953. 21 figures. 337pp. $6\frac{1}{8}$ x $9\frac{1}{4}$. S262 Paperbound **$2.25**

THERMODYNAMICS, Enrico Fermi. Unabridged reproduction of 1937 edition. Elementary in treatment; remarkable for clarity, organization. Requires no knowledge of advanced math beyond calculus, only familiarity with fundamentals of thermometry, calorimetry. Partial Contents: Thermodynamic systems; First & Second laws of thermodynamics; Entropy; Thermodynamic potentials: phase rule, reversible electric cell; Gaseous reactions: Van't Hoff reaction box, principle of LeChatelier; Thermodynamics of dilute solutions:: osmotic & vapor pressure, boiling & freezing points; Entropy constant. Index. 25 problems. 24 illustrations. x + 160pp. $5\frac{3}{8}$ x 8. S361 Paperbound **$1.75**

AN INTRODUCTION TO THE STUDY OF STELLAR STRUCTURE, Subrahmanyan Chandrasekhar. Outstanding treatise on stellar dynamics by one of world's greatest astrophysicists. Uses classical & modern math methods to examine relationship between loss of energy, the mass, and radius of stars in a steady state. Discusses thermodynamic laws from Caratheodory's axiomatic standpoint; adiabatic, polytropic laws; work of Ritter, Emden, Kelvin, others; Stroemgren envelopes as starter for theory of gaseous stars; Gibbs statistical mechanics (quantum); degenerate stellar configurations & theory of white dwarfs, etc. "Highest level of scientific merit," BULLETIN, AMER. MATH. SOC. Bibliography. Appendixes. Index. 33 figures. 509pp. $5\frac{3}{8}$ x 8. S413 Paperbound **$2.75**

APPLIED OPTICS AND OPTICAL DESIGN, A. E. Conrady. Thorough, systematic presentation of physical & mathematical aspects, limited mostly to "real optics." Stresses practical problem of maximum aberration permissible without affecting performance. All ordinary ray tracing methods; complete theory primary aberrations, enough higher aberration to design telescopes, low-powered microscopes, photographic equipment. Covers fundamental equations, extra-axial image points, transverse chromatic aberration, angular magnification, aplanatic optical systems, bending of lenses, oblique pencils, tolerances, secondary spectrum, spherical aberration (angular, longitudinal, transverse, zonal), thin lenses, dozens of similar topics. Index. Tables of functions of N. Over 150 diagrams. x + 518pp. 6⅛ x 9¼. S366 Paperbound **$2.95**

SPACE-TIME-MATTER, Hermann Weyl. "The standard treatise on the general theory of relativity," (Nature), written by a world-renowned scientists, provides a deep clear discussion of the logical coherence of the general theory, with introduction to all the mathematical tools needed: Maxwell, analytical geometry, non-Euclidean geometry, tensor calculus, etc. Basis is classical space-time, before absorption of relativity. Partial contents: Euclidean space, mathematical form, metrical continuum, relativity of time and space, general theory. 15 diagrams. Bibliography. New preface for this edition. xviii + 330pp. 5⅜ x 8. S267 Paperbound **$1.75**

RAYLEIGH'S PRINCIPLE AND ITS APPLICATION TO ENGINEERING, G. Temple & W. Bickley. Rayleigh's principle developed to provide upper and lower estimates of true value of fundamental period of a vibrating system, or condition of stability of elastic systems. Illustrative examples; rigorous proofs in special chapters. Partial contents: Energy method of discussing vibrations, stability. Perturbation theory, whirling of uniform shafts. Criteria of elastic stability. Application of energy method. Vibrating system. Proof, accuracy, successive approximations, application of Rayleigh's principle. Synthetic theorems. Numerical, graphical methods. Equilibrium configurations, Ritz's method. Bibliography. Index. 22 figures. ix + 156pp. 5⅜ x8.
S307 Paperbound **$1.50**

PHYSICS, ENGINEERING

THEORY OF VIBRATIONS, N. W. McLachlan. Based on an exceptionally successful graduate course given at Brown University, this discusses linear systems having 1 degree of freedom, forced vibrations of simple linear systems, vibration of flexible strings, transverse vibrations of bars and tubes, transverse vibration of circular plate, sound waves of finite amplitude, etc. Index. 99 diagrams. 160pp. 5⅜ x 8. S190 Paperbound **$1.35**

WAVE PROPAGATION IN PERIODIC STRUCTURES, L. Brillouin. A general method and application to different problems: pure physics, such as scattering of X-rays of crystals, thermal vibration in crystal lattices, electronic motion in metals; and also problems of electrical engineering. Partial contents: elastic waves in 1-dimensional lattices of point masses. Propagation of waves along 1-dimensional lattices. Energy flow. 2 dimensional, 3 dimensional lattices. Mathieu's equation. Matrices and propagation of waves along an electric line. Continuous electric lines. 131 illustrations. Bibliography. Index. xii + 253pp. 5⅜ x 8. S34 Paperbound **$1.85**

THE ELECTROMAGNETIC FIELD, Max Mason & Warren Weaver. Used constantly by graduate engineers. Vector methods exclusively: detailed treatment of electrostatics, expansion methods, with tables converting any quantity into absolute electromagnetic, absolute electrostatic, practical units. Discrete charges, ponderable bodies, Maxwell field equations, etc. Introduction. Indexes. 416pp. 5⅜ x 8. S185 Paperbound **$2.00**

APPLIED HYDRO- AND AEROMECHANICS by L. Prandtl and O. G. Tietjens. Presents, for the most part, methods which will be valuable to engineers. Covers flow in pipes, boundary layers, airfoil theory, entry conditions, turbulent flow in pipes and the boundary layer, determining drag from measurements of pressure and velocity, etc. "Will be welcomed by all students of aerodynamics," NATURE. Unabridged, unaltered. Index. 226 figures. 28 photographic plates illustrating flow patterns. xvi + 311pp. 5⅜ x 8. S375 Paperbound **$1.85**

FUNDAMENTALS OF HYDRO- AND AEROMECHANICS by L. Prandtl and O. G. Tietjens. The well-known standard work based upon Prandtl's unique insights and including original contributions of Tietjens. Wherever possible, hydrodynamic theory is referred to practical considerations in hydraulics with the view of unifying theory and experience through fundamental laws. Presentation is exceedingly clear and, though primarily physical, proofs are rigorous and use vector analysis to a considerable extent. Translated by L. Rosenhead. 186 figures. Index. xvi + 270pp. 5⅜ x 8. S374 Paperbound **$1.85**

DYNAMICS OF A SYSTEM OF RIGID BODIES (Advanced Section), E. J. Routh. Revised 6th edition of a classic reference aid. Much of its material remains unique. Partial contents: moving axes, relative motion, oscillations about equilibrium, motion. Motion of a body under no forces, any forces. Nature of motion given by linear equations and conditions of stability. Free, forced vibrations, constants of integration, calculus of finite differences, variations, procession and nutation, motion of the moon, motion of string, chain, membranes. 64 figures. 498pp. 5⅜ x 8.
S229 Paperbound **$2.35**

MECHANICS OF THE GYROSCOPE, THE DYNAMICS OF ROTATION, R. F. Deimel, Professor of Mechanical Engineering at Stevens Institute of Technology. Elementary general treatment of dynamics of rotation, with special application of gyroscopic phenomena. No knowledge of vectors needed. Velocity of a moving curve, acceleration to a point, general equations of motion, gyroscopic horizon, free gyro, motion of discs, the dammed gyro, 103 similar topics. Exercises. 75 figures. 208pp. 5⅜ x 8. S66 Paperbound **$1.65**

TABLES FOR THE DESIGN OF FACTORIAL EXPERIMENTS, Tosio Kitagawa and Michiwo Mitome. An invaluable aid for all applied mathematicians, physicists, chemists and biologists, this book contains tables for the design of factorial experiments. It covers Latin squares and cubes, factorial design, fractional replication in factorial design, factorial designs with split-plot confounding, factorial designs confounded in quasi-Latin squares, lattice designs, balanced incomplete block designs, and Youden's squares. New revised corrected edition, with explanatory notes. vii + 253pp. 7⅛ x 10. S437 Clothbound **$8.00**

NUMERICAL INTEGRATION OF DIFFERENTIAL EQUATIONS, Bennett, Milne & Bateman. Unabridged republication of original monograph prepared for National Research Council. New methods of integration of differential equations developed by 3 leading mathematicians: THE INTERPOLATIONAL POLYNOMIAL and SUCCESSIVE APPROXIMATIONS by A. A. Bennett; STEP-BY-STEP METHODS OF INTEGRATION by W. W. Milne; METHODS FOR PARTIAL DIFFERENTIAL EQUATIONS by H. Bateman. Methods for partial differential equations, transition from difference equations to differential equations, solution of differential equations to non-integral values of a parameter will interest mathematicians and physicists. 288 footnotes, mostly bibliographic; 235-item classified bibliography. 108pp. 5⅜ x 8. S305 Paperbound **$1.35**

DESIGN AND USE OF INSTRUMENTS AND ACCURATE MECHANISM, T. N. Whitehead. For the instrument designer, engineer; how to combine necessary mathematical abstractions with independent observation of actual facts. Partial contents: instruments & their parts, theory of errors, systematic errors, probability, short period errors, erratic errors, design precision, kinematic semi-kinematic design, stiffness, planning of an instrument, human factor, etc. Index. 85 photos, diagrams. xii + 288pp. 5⅜ x 8. S270 Paperbound **$1.95**

CHEMISTRY AND PHYSICAL CHEMISTRY

KINETIC THEORY OF LIQUIDS, J. Frenkel. Regarding the kinetic theory of liquids as a generalization and extension of the theory of solid bodies, this volume covers all types of arrangements of solids, thermal displacements of atoms, interstitial atoms and ions, orientational and rotational motion of molecules, and transition between states of matter. Mathematical theory is developed close to the physical subject matter. 216 bibliographical footnotes. 55 figures. xi + 485pp. 5⅜ x 8. S94 Clothbound **$3.95** / S95 Paperbound **$2.45**

THE PHASE RULE AND ITS APPLICATION, Alexander Findlay. Covering chemical phenomena of 1, 2, 3, 4, and multiple component systems, this "standard work on the subject" (NATURE, London), has been completely revised and brought up to date by A. N. Campbell and N. O. Smith. Brand new material has been added on such matters as binary, tertiary liquid equilibria, solid solutions in ternary systems, quinary systems of salts and water. Completely revised to triangular coordinates in ternary systems, clarified graphic representation, solid models, etc. 9th revised edition. Author, subject indexes. 236 figures. 506 footnotes, mostly bibliographic. xii + 494pp. 5⅜ x 8. S92 Paperbound **$2.45**

DYNAMICAL THEORY OF GASES, James Jeans. Divided into mathematical and physical chapters for the convenience of those not expert in mathematics, this volume discusses the mathematical theory of gas in a steady state, thermodynamics, Boltzmann and Maxwell, kinetic theory, quantum theory, exponentials, etc. 4th enlarged edition, with new material on quantum theory, quantum dynamics, etc. Indexes. 28 figures. 444pp. 6⅛ x 9¼. S136 Paperbound **$2.45**

POLAR MOLECULES, Pieter Debye. This work by Nobel laureate Debye offers a complete guide to fundamental electrostatic field relations, polarizability, molecular structure. Partial contents: electric intensity, displacement and force, polarization by orientation, molar polarization and molar refraction, halogen-hydrides, polar liquids, ionic saturation, dielectric constant, etc. Special chapter considers quantum theory. Indexed. 172pp. 5⅜ x 8. S63 Clothbound **$3.50** / S64 Paperbound **$1.50**

TREATISE ON THERMODYNAMICS, Max Planck. Based on Planck's original papers this offers a uniform point of view for the entire field and has been used as an introduction for students who have studied elementary chemistry, physics, and calculus. Rejecting the earlier approaches of Helmholtz and Maxwell, the author makes no assumptions regarding the nature of heat, but begins with a few empirical facts, and from these deduces new physical and chemical laws. 3rd English edition of this standard text by a Nobel laureate. xvi + 297pp. 5⅜ x 8. S219 Paperbound **$1.75**

ATOMIC SPECTRA AND ATOMIC STRUCTURE, G. Herzberg. Excellent general survey for chemists, physicists specializing in other fields. Partial contents: simplest line spectra and elements of atomic theory, multiple structure of line spectra and electron spin, building-up principle and periodic system of elements, finer details of atomic spectra, hyperfine structure of spectral lines, some experimental results and applications. Bibliography of 159 items. 80 figures. 20 tables. Index. xiii + 257pp. 5⅜ x 8. S115 Paperbound **$1.95**

EARTH SCIENCES

THE EVOLUTION OF THE IGNEOUS ROCKS, N. L. Bowen. Invaluable serious introduction applies techniques of physics and chemistry to explain igneous rocks diversity in terms of chemical composition and fractional crystallization. Discusses liquid immiscibility in silicate magmas, crystal sorting, liquid lines of descent, fractional resorption of complex minerals, petrogenesis, etc. Of prime importance to geologists & mining engineers, also to physicists, chemists working with high temperatures and pressures. "Most important," TIMES, London. 3 indexes. 263 bibliographic notes. 82 figures. xviii + 334pp. 5⅜ x 8. S311 Paperbound **$1.85**

GEOGRAPHICAL ESSAYS, William Morris Davis. Modern geography & geomorphology rests on the fundamental work of this scientist. 26 famous essays presenting most important theories, field researches. Partial contents: Geographical Cycle, Plains of Marine and Subaerial Denudation, The Peneplain, Rivers and Valleys of Pennsylvania, Outline of Cape Cod, Sculpture of Mountains by Glaciers, etc. "Long the leader and guide," ECONOMIC GEOGRAPHY. "Part of the very texture of geography . . . models of clear thought," GEOGRAPHIC REVIEW. Index. 130 figures. vi + 777pp. 5 3/8 x 8. S383 Paperbound **$2.95**

INTERNAL CONSTITUTION OF THE EARTH, edited by **Beno Gutenberg.** Completely revised, brought up-to-date, reset. Prepared for the National Research Council this is a complete & thorough coverage of such topics as earth origins, continent formation, nature & behavior of the earth's core, petrology of the crust, cooling forces in the core, seismic & earthquake material, gravity, elastic constants, strain characteristics and similar topics. "One is filled with admiration . . . a high standard . . . there is no reader who will not learn something from this book," London, Edinburgh, Dublin, Philosophic Magazine. Largest bibliography in print: 1127 classified items. Indexes. Tables of constants. 43 diagrams. 439pp. 6 1/8 x 9 1/4. S414 Paperbound **$2.45**

THE BIRTH AND DEVELOPMENT OF THE GEOLOGICAL SCIENCES, F. D. Adams. Most thorough history of the earth sciences ever written. Geological thought from earliest times to the end of the 19th century, covering over 300 early thinkers & systems: fossils & their explanation, vulcanists vs. neptunists, figured stones & paleontology, generation of stones, dozens of similar topics. 91 illustrations, including medieval, renaissance woodcuts, etc. Index. 632 footnotes, mostly bibliographical. 511pp. 5 3/8 x 8. T5 Paperbound **$2.00**

HYDROLOGY, edited by **Oscar E. Meinzer.** Prepared for the National Research Council. Detailed complete reference library on precipitation, evaporation, snow, snow surveying, glaciers, lakes, infiltration, soil moisture, ground water, runoff, drought, physical changes produced by water, hydrology of limestone terranes, etc. Practical in application, especially valuable for engineers. 24 experts have created "the most up-to-date, most complete treatment of the subject," AM. ASSOC. OF PETROLEUM GEOLOGISTS. Bibliography. Index. 165 illustrations. xi + 712pp. 6 1/8 x 9 1/4 S191 Paperbound **$2.95**

DE RE METALLICA, Georgius Agricola. 400-year old classic translated, annotated by former President Herbert Hoover. The first scientific study of mineralogy and mining, for over 200 years after its appearance in 1556, it was the standard treatise. 12 books, exhaustively annotated, discuss the history of mining, selection of sites, types of deposits, making pits, shafts, ventilating, pumps, crushing machinery; assaying, smelting, refining metals; also salt, alum, nitre, glass making. Definitive edition, with all 289 16th century woodcuts of the original. Bibliographical, historical introductions, bibliography, survey of ancient authors. Indexes. A fascinating book for anyone interested in art, history of science, geology, etc. DELUXE EDITION. 289 illustrations. 672pp. 6 3/4 x 10 3/4. Library cloth. S6 Clothbound **$10.00**

URANIUM PROSPECTING, H. L. Barnes. For immediate practical use, professional geologists considers uranium ores, geological occurrences, field conditions, all aspects of highly profitable occupation. Index. Bibliography. x +117pp. 5 3/8 x 8. T309 Paperbound **$1.00**

BIOLOGICAL SCIENCES

THE BIOLOGY OF THE AMPHIBIA, G. K. Noble, Late Curator of Herpetology at the Am. Mus. of Nat. Hist. Probably the most used text on amphibia, unmatched in comprehensiveness, clarity, detail. 19 chapters plus 85-page supplement cover development; heredity; life history; adaptation; sex, integument, respiratory, circulatory, digestive, muscular, nervous systems; instinct, intelligence habits environment economic value, relationships, classification, etc. "Nothing comparable to it," C. H. Pope, Curator of Amphibia, Chicago Mus. of Nat. Hist. 1047 bibliographic references. 174 illustrations. 600pp. 5 3/8 x 8. S206 Paperbound **$2.98**

THE BIOLOGY OF THE LABORATORY MOUSE, edited by **G. D. Snell.** 1st prepared in 1941 by the staff of the Roscoe B. Jackson Memorial laboratory, this is still the standard treatise on the mouse, assembling an enormous amount of material for which otherwise you would spend hours of research. Embryology, reproduction, histology, spontaneous neoplasms, gene & chromosomes mutations, genetics of spontaneous tumor formation, genetics of tumor formation, inbred, hybrid animals, parasites, infectious diseases, care & recording. Classified bibliography of 1122 items. 172 figures, including 128 photos. ix + 497pp. 6 1/8 x 9 1/4. S248 Clothbound **$6.00**

BEHAVIOR AND SOCIAL LIFE OF THE HONEYBEE, Ronald Ribbands. Oustanding scientific study; a compendium of practically everything known about social life of the honeybee. Stresses behavior of individual bees in field, hive. Extends von Frisch's experiments on communication among bees. Covers perception of temperature, gravity, distance, vibration; sound production; glands; structural differences; wax production, temperature regulation; recognition communication; drifting, mating behavior, other highly interesting topics. Bibliography of 690 references. Indexes. 127 diagrams, graphs, sections of bee anatomy, fine photographs. 352pp. S410 Clothbound **$4.50**

ELEMENTS OF MATHEMATICAL BIOLOGY, A. J. Lotka. A pioneer classic, the first major attempt to apply modern mathematical techniques on a large scale to phenomena of biology, biochemistry, psychology, ecology, similar life sciences. Partial Contents: Statistical meaning of irreversibility; Evolution as redistribution; Equations of kinetics of evolving systems; Chemical, interspecies equilibrium; parameters of state; Energy transformers of nature, etc. Can be read with profit even by those having no advanced math; unsurpassed as study-reference. Formerly titled ELEMENTS OF PHYSICAL BIOLOGY. 72 figures. xxx + 460pp. 5 3/8 x 8. S346 Paperbound **$2.45**

THE ORIGIN OF LIFE, A. I. Oparin. A classic of biology. This is the first modern statement of the theory of gradual evolution of life from nitrocarbon compounds. A brand-new evaluation of Oparin's theory in light of later research, by Dr. S. Margulis, University of Nebraska. xxv + 270pp. 5⅜ x 8.   S213 Paperbound **$1.75**

THE TRAVELS OF WILLIAM BARTRAM, edited by **Mark Van Doren.** This famous source-book of American anthropology, natural history, geography is the record kept by Bartram in the 1770's, on travels·through the wilderness of Florida, Georgia, the Carolinas. Containing accurate and beautiful descriptions of Indians, settlers, fauna, flora, it is one of the finest pieces of Americana ever written. Introduction by Mark Van Doren. 13 original illustrations. Index. 448pp. 5⅜ x 8.   T13 Paperbound **$2.00**

A SHORT HISTORY OF ANATOMY AND PHYSIOLOGY FROM THE GREEKS TO HARVEY, Charles Singer. Corrected edition of THE EVOLUTION OF ANATOMY, classic work tracing evolution of anatomy and physiology from prescientific times through Greek & Roman periods, Dark Ages, Renaissance, to age of Harvey and beginning of modern concepts. Centered on individuals, movements, periods that definitely advanced· anatomical knowledge: Plato, Diocles, Aristotle, Theophrastus, Herophilus, Erasistratus, the Alexandrians, Galen, Mondino, da Vinci, Linacre, Harvey, others. Special section on Vesalius; Vesalian atlas of nudes, skeletons, muscle tabulae. Index of names. 20 plates, 270 extremely interesting illustrations of ancient, medieval, renaissance, oriental origin. xii + 209pp. 5⅜ x 8.   T389 Paperbound **$1.75**

NEW BOOKS

LES METHODES NOUVELLES DE LA MÉCANIQUE CÉLESTE by H. Poincaré. Complete text (in French) of one of Poincaré's most important works. Revolutionized celestial mechanics: first use of integral invariants, first major application of linear differential equations, study of periodic orbits, lunar motion and Jupiter's satellites, three body problem, and many other important topics. "Started a new era . . . so extremely modern that even today few have mastered his weapons," E. T. Bell. Three volumes; 1282pp. 6⅛ x 9¼.

Vol. 1. S401 Paperbound **$2.75**
Vol. 2. S402 Paperbound **$2.75**
Vol. 3. S403 Paperbound **$2.75**

APPLICATIONS OF TENSOR ANALYSIS by A. J. McConnell. (Formerly, APPLICATIONS OF THE ABSOLUTE DIFFERENTIAL CALCULUS). An excellent text for understanding the application of tensor methods to familiar subjects such as: dynamics, electricity, elasticity, and hydrodynamics. It explains the fundamental ideas and notation of tensor theory, the geometrical treatment of tensor algebra, the theory of differentiation of tensors, and includes a wealth of practice material. Bibliography. Index. 43 illustrations. 685 problems. xii + 381pp.

S373 Paperbound **$1.85**

BRIDGES AND THEIR BUILDERS, David B. Steinman and Sara Ruth Watson. Engineers, historians, and everyone who has ever been fascinated by great spans will find this book an endless soúrce of information and interest. Dr. Steinman, the recent recipient of the Louis Levy Medal, is one of the great bridge architects and engineers of all time, and his analysis of the great bridges of all history is both authoritative and easily followed. Greek and Roman bridges, medieval bridges, oriental bridges, modern works such as the Brooklyn Bridge and the Golden Gate Bridge (and many others) are described in terms of history, constructional principles, artistry, and function. All in all this book is the most comprehensive and accurate semipopular history of bridges in print in English. New greatly revised enlarged edition. 23 photographs, 26 line drawings. Index. xvii + 401pp. 5⅜ x 8.   T431 Paperbound **$1.95**

MATHEMATICS IN ACTION, O. G. Sutton. Excellent middle-level exposition of application of advanced mathematics to the study of the universe. The author demonstrates how mathematics is applied in ballistics, theory of computing machines, waves and wavelike phenomena, theory of fluid flow, meterological problems, statistics, flight, and similar phenomena. No knowledge of advanced mathematics is necessary to·follow the author's presentation. Differential equations, Fourier series, group concepts, eigen functions, Planck's constant, airfoil theory and similar topics are explained so clearly in everyday language that almost anyone can derive benefit from reading this book. 2nd edition. Index. 88 figures. viii + 236pp. 5⅜ x 8.

T450 Clothbound **$3.50**

MATHEMATICAL FOUNDATIONS OF INFORMATION THEORY by A. I. Khinchin. For the first time, mathematicians, statisticians, physicists, cyberneticists and communications engineers are offered a complete and exact introduction to this relatively young field. Entropy as a measure of a finite "scheme," applications to coding theory, study of sources, channels and codes, detailed proofs of both Shannon theorems for any ergodic source and any stationary channel with finite memory, and much more is covered. Bibliography. vii + 120pp. 5⅜ x 8.

S434 Paperbound **$1.35**